Paintings and Textiles of the
BASS MUSEUM OF ART

Bass Museum of Art, Miami Beach, Florida

PAINTINGS AND TEXTILES OF THE
BASS MUSEUM OF ART
Selections from the Collection

Margarita A. Russell

With Contributions by
Gerbert Frodl, Kenneth Garlick, Deborah Kraak,
Perri Lee Roberts, Alice Zrebiec

Bass Museum of Art

Miami Beach, Florida
1990

Editor: Margarita A. Russell
Design and Production: Tom Gormley, Miami, Florida
Production Assistant: Renée Solomon, Miami, Florida
Production Staff: Trudy Chang and Deborah Gormley, Miami, Florida
Typesetting: BoldType, Inc., Coral Gables, Florida
Photography: Ira Victor, Miami Beach, Florida
Printing and Color Separations: LDC Graphics, Miami, Florida
Binding: Nicholstone Binding, Nashville, Tennessee

Printed in Garamond No. 3 on Reflections 110 lb. Text.
Cover: Ferdinand Bol, *Venus and Adonis,* 79.131

This catalogue was supported in part by grants from the National
Endowment for the Arts, a Federal agency.

The Bass Museum of Art is recognized by the State of Florida as a Major
Cultural Institution and receives major funding from the State of Florida
through the Florida Department of State, the Florida Arts Council and
the Division of Cultural Affairs. Major support is provided by the City of
Miami Beach and Friends of the Bass Museum. The Museum also receives
funding from the Dade County Cultural Affairs Council, the Visitor and
Convention Authority, and the Institute of Museum Services.

LIBRARY OF CONGRESS CATALOGUE CARD NUMBER 90-82402

Printed in the United States of America

Accredited by the
American Association
of Museums

Paintings and Textiles of the
BASS MUSEUM OF ART

Contents

JOHN AND JOHANNA BASS, PATRONS OF THE ARTS

Born in Vienna, Austria, in 1891, John Bass was talented both musically and artistically and wanted to study art, but his father, a commercial counselor to the Emperor of Austria, advised him to make money first and sent him to business school. Moving to New York in 1914, he made a brief effort to earn his living there as a pianist, but lack of success soon convinced him to follow in his father's footsteps and choose the art of business. Starting as an errand boy on Wall Street, he went on to become the president of the Wall Street firm of L. W. and P. Armstrong as well as one of the leading figures in the sugar industry.

A man of lively intelligence, John Bass continued to exercise his many and varied talents while pursuing his business career. A composer of over fifty published compositions, he also played the piano in chamber-music groups. Moreover he described himself as a painter in the style of the French Impressionists, and his interest in photography led to patented inventions in that field. In addition, he was a writer, etcher, world traveller, art collector, and eventually a noted philanthropist, sharing his collections with a number of institutions although the principal recipient was, of course, the Bass Museum.

Johanna, his wife, was also talented and creative. She wrote poetry, performed with her husband on matching concert grand pianos they had purchased for the museum, and was largely responsible for the building's original decor. A charming and gracious woman, she often personally welcomed visitors to the museum and together the Basses presided over cultural events arranged in its galleries. Their collaboration contributed to the cultural growth of the Miami Beach community, and its citizens and the thousands of visitors to the museum are their true beneficiaries.

Mrs. Bass died in 1970 and Mr. Bass in 1978. They had three sons—Eric, Roger, and Robert—each of whom, in addition to his other accomplishments, is also a highly talented musician. Roger and Robert serve as museum trustees.

FOREWORD AND ACKNOWLEDGEMENTS

In 1964 John and Johanna Bass donated their old master collection to the city of Miami Beach, a generous gift which has brought pleasure and enlightenment to many thousands of visitors. The collection of more than five-hundred European works from the fifteenth to the early twentieth century, including an important group of more than two-hundred paintings and significant holdings of textiles and sculpture, provided a solid foundation on which to develop a major institution with one of the most comprehensive collections of European art in the Southeast.

The present volume is the culmination of an extensive body of research conducted over the past four years. A representative selection of paintings and textiles from the original Bass gift have been included. A publication on aspects of the sculpture, decorative arts and works on paper is proposed for the future.

We take particular satisfaction that through this catalogue the most up-to-date scholarship on the permanent collection can be widely shared with specialists and the interested public. Moreover, the information developed during this project enables us to provide richer interpretation within the museum and to exhibit its fine permanent collection more effectively than had been previously possible.

Preparation of this catalogue has been achieved through the efforts of Margarita Russell, Curator of Research, who ably coordinated and edited the publication while at the same time contributing the major entries on the northern European works. We have been fortunate to enlist the participation of national and international scholars, a number of whom provided special review on site. Perri Lee Roberts of the University of Miami; Gerbert Frodl of the Österreichische Galerie, Vienna; Kenneth Garlick of Oxford University; Deborah Kraak and Alice Zrebiec, textile experts from the Museum of Fine Arts, Boston, and the Metropolitan Museum of Art, New York, wrote the catalogue entries to works within their spheres of expertise. Egbert Haverkamp Begemann from the Institute of Fine Arts, New York University, visited the museum, examining the paintings and generously offering advice not only on research matters but also on the museum's potential as a scholarly institution. We are deeply indebted to them and to others too numerous to mention here, who responded to occasional inquiries and whose efforts are acknowledged in footnotes accompanying the text.

The project would not have been possible without the generous financial support of the National Endowment for the Arts (for both the research and the publication phases) and a technical assistance grant from the Art Museum Association, now the American Federation of the Arts. We are also grateful to Friends of the Bass Museum, our private support arm; the City of Miami Beach, our parent organization; Metro-Dade Cultural Affairs Council; and the State of Florida Division of Cultural Affairs which through its major-institution program provides generous annual operating support to the Bass Museum of Art.

Diane W. Camber
Executive Director

Museum Programs

Exhibitions

Throughout the year, quality special exhibitions are organized to bring a wide range of visual programs to members and public which complement the permanent collection. These temporary exhibitions bring the visual arts from nationally and internationally renowned sources to the community on a regular basis.

Museum Education

Thousands of public school children tour the museum annually. In addition, students and interns of more than seven colleges and universities in the region extensively use the collection and programs as a resource. A year-round provision of lectures, films and concerts for adults is an integral part of programming.

Museum Shop

A select array of art-oriented gifts including the original creations of artists and designers is available through the museum shop.

Museum School

The Bass Museum of Art operates the county's only museum school with instruction in painting, sculpture, ceramics, jewelry, and textiles for all ages throughout the year. The faculty is comprised of professional artists.

Future Plans

A planned renovation and expansion of the museum's historic art deco structure built in 1930 as a city library and art center will enable more of the original Bass bequest to be on view, provide for better conservation and storage of the permanent collection, permit a growing collection to be adequately exhibited and allow for expanded temporary exhibitions and educational programs.

INTRODUCTION

John Bass's love of art was not confined to one particular field, and the collection he donated to the city of Miami Beach reflects the variety of his interests. A gifted painter himself, painting was clearly his foremost concern, and the paintings are the heart of the collection. Textiles, sculptures, and decorative objects add variety.

The collection, which contains outstanding examples in each category, has never before been subjected to scholarly study, and no critical catalogue has previously been attempted. The majority of works, numbering 502, are listed in *The John and Johanna Bass Collection*, a catalogue last issued in 1973 (an earlier edition is undated). This publication contains only a brief entry for each work, with attributions according to the information available at that time.

It would have been overly ambitious to attempt a study of the entire collection all at once. Since the paintings and textiles are its greatest strength, the director and editor decided to begin with a catalogue of these two subjects.

The paintings Mr. Bass selected are mostly of European origin, and the emphasis on the northern schools reflects his lasting affection for his country of birth, Austria. A selection of seventeenth-century painting of the Netherlands (Rubens, Seghers, Cornelis van Haarlem, Ferdinand Bol and others) is supplemented by Netherlandish and Germanic works of the fifteenth and sixteenth centuries.

The nineteenth- and early twentieth-century paintings particularly bear witness to Mr. Bass's continued links with Austria. The Bass Museum probably has a more representative group of Austrian paintings, including local schools, than any other collection in the United States. For a long time the nineteenth- and twentieth-century Austrian and German paintings remained shrouded in obscurity; they are only now beginning to attract scholarly attention. We have been fortunate to secure the collaboration of Dr. Gerbert Frodl from the Österreichische Galerie in Vienna, author of a recent monograph on the famous Austrian painter Hans Makart, whose masterpiece, *The Valkyrie*, is owned by the Bass Museum. Dr. Frodl is thoroughly familiar with the Austrian painters represented in the collection and was able to identify the subjects of individual portraits.

The textiles collection, too, reflects Mr. Bass's great interest in Austrian art. The important group of ecclesiastical needlework contains the spectacular series of late seventeenth-century church vestments called the *Rosenornat* and the eighteenth-century *Maria Theresia Ornat*, commissioned by that Empress. Other masterpieces in the textiles collection are the famous sixteenth-century Flemish tapestry *The Tournament* and two huge nineteenth-century tapestries, called *The Hunt*, by French designer Louis-Marie Baader, which fill two walls in a major gallery of the museum specially built to provide the space for hanging these monumental works.

Research on the earlier paintings in the collection was difficult because of the absence of records for many works, but the quality and rarity of these paintings made the time-consuming search for clues and connections worthwhile.

Like most collections, the Bass Museum's collection had its share of misattributions. It has been the objective of the authors of this catalogue to investigate carefully each attribution and make corrections wherever appropriate. The process of reassessment has not invariably resulted in the 'down-grading' of works from well-known masters to followers or imitators. In a number of cases, works recently given to 'school of' or 'follower of' have been securely attributed to the master in question, or to another artist.

Our investigation has established that Mr. Bass took great care in assembling his collection. Whenever possible, before making a purchase he consulted the leading experts to obtain the best information available. In the following decades, however, scholarship in the various fields of art history has made enormous strides. Our reattributions, which are summarized in an index, reflect the latest research.

Work on the catalogue has led to many ideas for future acquisitions. Some subjects, such as landscape, seascape, genre, and still-life could be expanded. Judicious acquisitions within these areas would strengthen the collection and its scholarly and aesthetic value.

Conservation is an ongoing process. Most of the old master paintings have been surveyed, and conservation reports are available to scholars and experts on request. Recent successful restorations include the *Venus and Adonis* by Ferdinand Bol (79.131), the portrait of *Lucius Concannon, M.P.* by John Hoppner (79.321), and the family portrait of *Sir Charles Cockerell* by Sir Thomas Lawrence (63.34). The cleaning and restoring of paintings will continue according to plan. Condition reports in the catalogue have accordingly been kept very brief; they are to be found at the end of each entry.

Apart from the invaluable contributions made by the scholars who participated in the research and wrote the entries for the catalogue, many experts have generously given their time to help with problems. I am particularly grateful for advice and suggestions from Egbert Haverkamp Begemann, Julius S. Held, Arthur Wheelock, Oliver Millar, Edward J. Sullivan, and Larry Silver, to name just a few. I am also greatly indebted for research facilities and invaluable cooperation from the National Gallery of Art, Washington, D.C. and its former chief librarian, J.M. Edelstein and his staff, and to the Frick Reference Library, the De Witt Library, and the library and curatorial departments of the Victoria and Albert

Museum. Particular thanks are due to Christopher Brown for allowing me to use the Reference Library of the National Gallery, London, and to Elspeth Hector and her colleagues for their efficient and friendly help while I was working there. I am also very grateful to B. Niewenhuis of the Rijksbureau voor Kunsthistorische Documentatie (RKD) in The Hague for the indispensable resources made available, and to G. Kotting, whose generous help enabled me to complete my research there within the limited time at my disposal. The expert assistance and courtesy received from Maxim Préaux at the Bibliothèque Nationale and from Jacques Foucart and his colleagues at the Louvre in Paris are also gratefully acknowledged. The Richter Library of the University of Miami and, in particular, Mrs. Mildred Merrick have been unfailingly helpful and interested in my research. Special credit is due for their friendly assistance.

Denise M. Gerson assisted with research on the French Impressionist paintings and Arch Angelus Sturaitis assisted with the preparation of the manuscript during the final months of the research period, which came to an end in April 1987. Gloria Jackson was a most efficient and dedicated editorial assistant, who saw the manuscript through its many revisions and helped prepare it for publication. Perri Lee Roberts, one of the contributors to the catalogue, also generously gave her time as proofreader and participated in numerous staff meetings, contributing many excellent ideas in editing and design. Tom Gormley contributed his special expertise as design consultant, and Lois Fern did an excellent job as copy editor. Donald P. Kahn, board member of The Bass Museum of Art, contributed his expertise and generosity on typography.

Stanley S. Robinson, frames conservator at the National Gallery of Art, Washington, D.C., examined many of the frames of paintings in the collection. Some are rare examples of outstanding quality. Robinson's findings are included in catalogue entries wherever relevant. Full reports are accessible to experts if required.

Margarita A. Russell
Editor

CONTRIBUTORS TO THE CATALOGUE

	Initials	Subject
Gerbert Frodl, Österreichische Galerie, Vienna.*	G.F.	Austrian-German nineteenth-century painting
Kenneth J. Garlick, Balliol College, Oxford University	K.J.G.	English portraits, eighteenth/nineteenth centuries
Deborah E. Kraak, Museum of Fine Arts, Boston	D.E.K.	The *Tournament* tapestry
Perri Lee Roberts, University of Miami	P.L.R.	Italian Renaissance painting
Margarita A. Russell, Bass Museum of Art	M.A.R.	Seventeenth-century northern painting and selected other works
Alice M. Zrebiec, Metropolitan Museum of Art, New York	A.M.Z.	Textiles (except the *Tournament* tapestry)

Dr. Frodl's catalogue entries were written in German and translated into English by Margarita Russell.

BIOGRAPHICAL NOTES

Dr. Gerbert Frodl is currently curator of nineteenth- and twentieth-century paintings in the Österreichische Galerie (Schloss Belvedere), Vienna, Austria. He has published widely in the field of Austrian and mid-European art. His major publications include *Hans Makart—Monographie und Werkverzeichnis,* Salzburg 1974; *Kunst in Wien um 1900, Die andere Seite,* Halbturn (Österreichische Galerie) 1987; *Wiener Malerei der Biedermeierzeit,* Rosenheim 1987; *Gustav Klimt, Das Beethovenfries,* Salzburg 1987.

Dr. Kenneth J. Garlick, keeper of Western art at the Ashmolean Museum, Oxford University, until 1985, is currently Fellow Emeritus of Balliol College, Oxford University. He has published the authoritative monograph on Sir Thomas Lawrence (q.v.) and has recently completed a comprehensive catalogue of his paintings for the Phaidon Press. Other publications include a catalogue of the paintings in the Spencer Collection at Althorp, England, and numerous articles and book reviews.

Deborah E. Kraak is assistant curator of textiles and costumes at the Museum of Fine Arts, Boston. She specializes in tapestries, eighteenth-century costume, and ecclesiastical vestments. Currently she is preparing the English text of the volume on paraments and vestments for the *Glossarium Artis* series. An entry on Western religious dress was her contribution to the recently published *Encyclopedia of Religion.*

Dr. Perri Lee Roberts is an assistant professor in the Department of Art History, University of Miami. Her monograph on Masolino da Panicale is to be published shortly by Oxford University Press.

Dr. Margarita A. Russell, editor and coordinator of research for the catalogue, came to the Bass Museum as a visiting curator of research after completing a senior fellowship at the Center for Advanced Study in the Visual Arts, National Gallery of Art, Washington, D.C. She is author of a monograph on Dutch seventeenth-century marine paintings (*Visions of the Sea: Hendrick C. Vroom and the Origins of Dutch Marine Painting,* Leiden University Press 1983) and of numerous other publications in the field of sixteenth- and seventeenth-century northern European art. She is director of a museum interns program at the Bass Museum of Art for the University of Miami, where she also serves as adjunct professor to the Department of Art History.

Dr. Alice Zrebiec is curator of European textiles, tapestries, vestments and fans, Renaissance through nineteenth century, at the Metropolitan Museum of Art, New York. She has published widely in her field and delivered papers and lectures at major museums and professional symposia.

NOTES TO THE CATALOGUE

The catalogue is organized into separate sections for paintings and textiles. Because the textile entries do not usually involve individual artists' names, they are arranged chronologically. The painting entries, alphabetically arranged, are separated chronologically into two groups: pre-1840 and post-1840, a division which best suits the content of the collection. Anonymous artists are listed by their country, region, or traditional designation, such as "Master of the Revaler St. Elizabeth Legend." Named painters are given brief biographical notes, followed by entries for each work of theirs included in the collection. Each title is accompanied by the Bass Museum's accession number.

Attributions involving varying degrees of relationship to a known artist are specified as follows:

Studio of/Workshop of:

Done by assistants in the master's studio/workshop to the master's own design and under his supervision.

Follower of:

An unknown artist strongly influenced by the style of a named master, not necessarily working at the same place or at the same time.

Circle of:

An unknown contemporary artist working in proximity to the named master and influenced by his ideas.

Style of/Manner of:

Work done in the style of a named master to the exclusion of individual creativity, but not with an intention to deceive. The intention to deceive is usually indicated by the term "Imitator of."

School of:

Refers to a town or region identified with certain common artistic characteristics.

In the entries for the paintings, the medium is oil unless otherwise stated. Measurements are exclusive of frames and are given in centimeters, followed by inches in parentheses. Height precedes width. Left and right refer to the viewer's left and right unless otherwise stated.

Notes on the technical condition of a painting, except in some special cases, are kept as brief as possible. They are mostly omitted for nineteenth- and twentieth-century paintings.

Notes on frames are included only when the frame is of special interest, or in the case of altarpieces where it forms an integral part of the composition.

The **Provenance** includes dealers and auctions. **References** are confined to major publications, with the addition of unpublished manuscript sources where necessary. Sales and exhibition catalogues are not included in this section but are listed in the **Provenance** and **Exhibitions** sections.

M.A.R.

WORKS EXECUTED BEFORE 1840

ANTWERP SCHOOL, Attributed to

First half of the sixteenth century

Fragment of a Crucifixion (63.18)

Painted c. 1530.
Tempera (some oil) on panel, *60.9 x 69.2 (23¾ x 27)*

Provenance
Bass Collection, 1963.

References
Bass Catalogue 1973, No. 18 (Heinrich Aldegrever, attr.)

The panel was previously attributed to the German master Heinrich Aldegrever (1502-1558), but the attribution cannot be reconciled with Aldegrever's painting style. The character of this composition clearly points to Antwerp in the early sixteenth century, but certain Germanic traits are present, such as the hardness of the outlines, the emphasis on ornamentation, and some of the facial types. Connections with various artists have been suggested, such as Gossaert (early), Van Orley, Coecke van Aelst, and Jean Bellegambe, but none of these artists' works is close enough to the Bass panel.

A striking oddity of the composition is the missing third cross. The lower part of the cross carrying Christ is flanked on the left by the lower part of the cross carrying one of the crucified thieves, but there is no trace of the cross with the second thief. This is an unprecedented deviation from the traditional iconography of the Crucifixion, which shows Christ either on the cross alone, or flanked by the crosses with the two thieves. Since the upper part of the left cross with the tied feet of the thief is contained in the insert, and the lower part is overpainted, it must be assumed that this cross is a later addition. The original composition would have shown only one cross, with the figure of Christ.

Stylistically the harsh outlines of the figures are in sharp contrast with the painterly Patinier-like landscape in the background. It seems possible that the landscape was painted by a different hand. Another peculiarity is the modeling of the figures in strong hatching and cross-hatching, suggestive of an engraving rather than a painting technique. The veins and muscles of the massive soldier on the left are delineated so prominently as if intended for an anatomy lesson. The identity of the master (or masters) of the Bass Crucifixion fragment is currently an unsolved mystery.

M.A.R.

Condition: The fragment has suffered damage at the top. There are two major cracks at 10″ and 20″ from the left edge, perhaps old joints that have opened. An insert at top left is visible from the front and back. It contains a section of the left cross with the feet of the thief tied against it. The lower portion of the cross beneath the insert is overpainted.

5

AUSTRIAN OR SOUTH GERMAN SCHOOL (Salzburg or Passau), Attributed to

Last quarter of the fifteenth century

Christ Brought Before Caiaphas (79.133)

Tempera on panel, *80.7 x 60.3 (31½ x 23).*

Provenance
Galerie Fischer, Luzern, 1965.

References
Prof. E. Schaffran, Vienna, Certificate, 22 May 1961
(as Gabriel Maleskircher).
Bass Catalogue 1973, No. 133 (Gabriel Maleskircher).
Dr. Karl Schütz, Kunsthistorisches Museum, Vienna,
Letter to the Bass Museum, 13 February 1987.

The scene shows Christ after his arrest in the Garden of
Gethsemane being led with bound hands before the High
Priest Caiaphas, who passes judgment on him. One of the
soldiers is about to strike him, another carries a flag with
a scorpion, the symbol of the Israelites.[1] It is one of the
traditional scenes in the cycle of the Passion. The panel
was previously attributed to Gabriel Maleskircher
(c. 1448-1495), but Karl Schütz and other scholars now
believe it was painted in the region of Salzburg or Passau,
c. 1480 (see ref. Schütz).

M.A.R.

1. See Herder, *Lexikon der Christlichen Ikonographie,* vol. IV, 1972,
   pp. 170-71.

Condition: The panel has probably been cut on all sides and the bottom third is mostly repainted. The upper portion is in a much better state of preservation.
The harsh black outlines around hair and figures are due to overpainting.

GIOVANNI BARBAGELATA

Italian, active 1484-1508

Giovanni Barbagelata was a late fifteenth-century Genoese painter who produced a number of large altarpieces. Nothing is known about his early years, but he probably received his training from Giovanni Mazone (1433-1511), who was the outstanding local master in Genoa. Barbagelata is recorded as working in Mazone's shop in 1485. His mature works reflect the influence of Mazone and the Lombard painters Vincenzo Foppa (1427/30-1515/16) and Carlo Braccesco (active 1478-1484), and, to a lesser extent, that of the Flemish artist Gerard David (active 1484-1523).[1] Barbagelata's style was more conservative than that of his fellow Genoese painters.

Polyptych: The Madonna and Child Enthroned with Music-Making Angels and St. Francis of Assisi, St. Bonaventura, St. Peter, St. John the Baptist, St. Bernardino of Siena, and St. Louis of Toulouse; [in the pinnacles] The Annunciation, The Crucifixion (63.17)

Tempera on panel, *279.9 x 224.3 (108 x 87½).*
Except for the unadorned area of the upper portion of the altarpiece—which is a modern replacement for lost fretwork, such as that found in the lower half—the frame is original and is typical of late-fifteenth-century Piedmontese painting. A comparable frame may be seen in Giovanni Mazone's *Annunciation* altarpiece in Santa Maria di Castello, Genoa.

Provenance
Convent of the Recollects, Corvara, Corsica.
Galerie Charpentier, Paris; sold 16 March 1959, No. 77 (as School of Vivarini).
Bass Collection, before 1963.

References
B. Fredericksen and F. Zeri, *Census of Pre-Nineteenth Century Italian Paintings in North American Public Collections,* Cambridge, Mass., 1972, p. 123 (as Giovanni Massone {sic}).
Bass Catalogue 1973, No. 17 (as Giovanni Massoni {sic}).

The Bass altarpiece has been attributed by Roberto Longhi (Bass Catalogue 1973) to Giovanni Mazone, but the more likely artist responsible for the work is Giovanni Barbagelata. Typical of Barbagelata's style, and not of Mazone's, is the use of an extensive gold background, the few elements of setting, the limited range of tonal gradations, the more simplified drapery patterns, and the woodenness of the figures. A work comparable in style is his *Madonna of the Victory* (Genoa, Oratorio della Vittoria) of c. 1503. But here, as in many other of Barbagelata's works, he clearly imitated Mazone both in regard to individual figures and overall composition (cf. Mazone's

triptych of *St. Ludwig* [Moneglia, S. Giorgio]; or, *St. Mark Enthroned with Sts. Catherine, John the Baptist, Paul and Giustina* {Liverpool, Walker Art Gallery]). The type of the throne and the music-making angels in the central panel of the Bass altarpiece specifically recall the work of Vincenzo Foppa, who worked in Genoa and nearby Savona in the years 1461-1490, and whose paintings were another important source of inspiration for the less-talented Barbagelata (cf. Foppa's *Madonna and Child Enthroned with Music-Making Angels* [Brera, Milan] of 1476, formerly in S.M. delle Grazie, Milan; it dates to the same period as Foppa's lost polyptych for S. Domenico, Genoa).

The Bass polyptych originally belonged to the convent of the Recollects, a reformed branch of the Franciscan order, in Corvara, Corsica. It is one of two works painted by Barbagelata for the island of Corsica which, as of 1453, was nominally a Genoese dependency. It is interesting to note that in the case of the other altarpiece (signed and dated 1498; today in the parochial church of Calvi, Corsica), the painter was specifically instructed by the patron to copy Mazone's altarpiece in S. Maria di Castello, Genoa.[2]

The subject matter of the central panels, the Madonna and Child enthroned flanked by saints, was one of the most common devotional images of fourteenth- and fifteenth-century Italian painting. Reflecting the Franciscan patronage of the work, four of the six saints included in the painting are prominent Franciscans: to the left of the Madonna are St. Francis of Assisi, the founder of the order, and St. Bonaventura, who wrote the first biography of St. Francis; to the right are St. Bernardino of Siena, the greatest Franciscan of the fifteenth century, and St. Louis of Toulouse, a thirteenth-century nobleman who renounced his claim to the throne of Naples in order to become a Franciscan friar. Next to the Madonna are St. John the Baptist and St. Peter who is shown holding the keys to heaven. They were probably chosen for the altarpiece because of their symbolic associations with baptism and redemption. In the pinnacles of the polyptych are scenes from the beginning and the end of

9

Christ's life, the Annunciation and the Crucifixion, which symbolically represent the promise of mankind's salvation and its ultimate fulfillment.

The format of the altarpiece with saints occupying panels separate from the Madonna and Child, the elaborate nature of the framework, the use of a gold ground, flat disk-shaped halos, gold striations on the draperies, and embossed surface decoration, are features of the work which reflect the conservative taste of the patron and the provincial style of the painter. Elsewhere in Italy such stylistic features were considered archaic by the end of the fifteenth century and were not generally employed.

However, certain other elements of the work do reveal that Barbagelata was influenced by contemporary Renaissance painting. These features include the classicizing architecture of the throne, the use of the contrapposto stance, and the limited suggestion of three-dimensional space evident in the two panels of the Annunciation.

P.L.R.

1. G. V. Castelnovi, "Giovanni Barbagelata," *Bolletino d'arte*, 4, 1951, pp. 212-13.
2. G. V. Castelnovi, "Un politico del Barbagelata in Corsica," *Bollettino ligustico per la storia regionale*, 4, 1950, n.p.

Condition: On the whole, the three central panels of the polyptych are in good condition; the three panels of the pinnacles are overpainted.

THOMAS BARKER

English, 1769-1847

The landscape and genre painter Thomas Barker was born near Pontypool and, when still a child, moved with his family to Bath, where he remained for the rest of his life. A local patron sent the talented young artist to Rome for three years, 1790-1793. Barker was a self-taught artist, but became very popular and successful as a painter of rustic scenes, some of which were used for the decoration of Worcester china. His style is clearly influenced by the landscapes and 'fancy' pictures of Thomas Gainsborough, who had worked in Bath from 1760 to 1774. Like Gainsborough, Barker was initially attracted to Dutch seventeenth-century landscape painting, and he seems to have been inspired in Rome by the poetic light effects of Claude Lorrain.

Pastoral (64.112)

Canvas, *96.5 x 132 (38 x 28).*

Provenance
Thomas Emerson, Esq., Portsmouth, England.
Bass Collection, 1964.

References
Bass Catalogue 1973, No. 112 (as George Morland, attr.).

The painting shows a country girl dreamily resting under a massive tree, while a young rustic watches her from beyond a fence. The picture was previously attributed to George Morland but a reattribution of this attractive arcadian landscape to Thomas Barker carries more conviction. The distribution of light and shade, the treatment of clouds and of trees silhouetted against a brightly lit horizon, compare well with known paintings by the artist, for instance the *Landscape with Travellers* in the Victoria Art Gallery, Bath, No. 62-1. M.A.R.

Condition: In good condition.

FERDINAND BOL

Dutch, 1616-1680

Ferdinand Bol, son of Balthasar Bol, was baptized at Dordrecht, 24 June 1616. At a young age he became a pupil of Rembrandt in Amsterdam and many of his early works are close to the manner of the master. Bol was one of the most talented and distinguished of Rembrandt's pupils. He was particularly successful as a portraitist, but he also painted 'history' pictures, i.e. historical, religious, and mythological subjects, for public buildings in Amsterdam and other Dutch cities. He was one of the painters chosen to decorate the new Amsterdam town hall in the late 1650s. One of his pupils, Gottfried Kneller, became court painter to the English king Charles II.

Venus and Adonis (79.131)

Signed and dated bottom left: *Bol fecit 1661.*
Canvas, *200 x 222 (78 x 87).*

Provenance

Private collection Budapest, 1902 (see ref. Pigler).
Private collection M., Hungary, 1936-1945, later New York.
Galerie Fischer, Luzern, 1961; sold 27 July 1965.
The Bass Museum Catalogue 1973 lists the collection of Count Ferdinand Lavaux of Czechoslovakia (no dates). However, no related documentation can be found. The provenance given by Blankert (who corresponded with Mr. Bass in 1968) is therefore accepted here.

References

A. Pigler, *Barockthemen,* Budapest 1956, vol. II, p. 242, ill. p. 243.
Catalogue Galerie Fischer, Luzern, 21-26 November 1961.
Reproduction, *Die Weltkunst,* 1 November 1961.
Bass Catalogue 1973, No. 131.
Albert Blankert, *Ferdinand Bol (1616-1680), Rembrandt's Pupil,* Doornspijk 1982, cat. 31, pl. 40; text pp. 47, 49, 63.
Peter C. Sutton, *Dutch Art in America,* Grand Rapids 1986, p. 152, fig. 221.

The painting illustrates a story from Ovid's *Metamorphoses,* one of the most popular literary sources for Baroque painters. Venus, goddess of love, stricken by Cupid's arrow, had fallen deeply in love with the beautiful youth Adonis, son of the incestuous relationship of King Cinyras of Paphos and his daughter Myrrha. Bol's painting shows the scene where Adonis, holding a spear and accompanied by his dog, is about to leave the goddess for the hunt. Venus, assisted by Cupid, tries in vain to detain her lover who, as she foresees, will soon be killed by a wild boar. Bol's composition symbolically anticipates the hero's death by including the anemones (under Venus' right foot) which sprouted from the spot where Adonis' blood touched the ground.

The Bass picture belongs to the artist's mature period, dating from the 1650s when, like other Rembrandt pupils, (see Flinck, Cat. 63.12), he broke with his teacher's more introspective style and embraced a dynamic and decorative high baroque manner.

The Bass painting belongs to a series of mythological scenes by Bol, all depicting amorous episodes, mostly in a landscape setting. This series was inspired by similar erotic-pastoral cycles painted by Rubens and his followers in Flanders. According to Blankert, Bol's series culminates in the Bass painting, which is the only fully dated example and the most dynamically baroque in style (Blankert, pp. 47, 63). The coloristic beauty and compositional harmony of the painting, with its poetic landscape background, make this an acknowledged masterpiece of the artist.

M.A.R.

Condition: Cleaned and re-lined in 1987. In excellent condition.

SANDRO BOTTICELLI
Italian, 1444-1510

DOMENICO GHIRLANDAIO
Italian, 1449-1494

Sandro Botticelli (born Alessandro di Moriano Filipepi) was one of the leading artists working in Florence in the last quarter of the fifteenth century. He received his training from Fra Filippo Lippi (c. 1406-1469), whose influence endured throughout the younger artist's career. Like Lippi, Botticelli was a masterful draftsman who delighted in the use of sinuous line and decorative surface pattern. His output included both panel paintings and frescos, religious works and portraits; however he is best known for the series of mythological works which he painted in the 1470s and 1480s for the elite circle of Florentine neo-Platonists who gathered around the humanist philosopher Marsilio Ficino. Although there is no solid evidence to support Vasari's claim that Botticelli, towards the end of his life, became a follower of Savonarola, it is true that his paintings of the 1490s take on an increased sense of religious fervor. After 1501, until his death in 1510, Botticelli appears to have done little painting.

Domenico Ghirlandaio (born Domenico de Tommaso Bigordi) headed the most popular workshop of late fifteenth-century Florence. Ghirlandaio's stylistic origins are uncertain, but he was probably trained by the minor Florentine painter Alesso Baldovinetti (c. 1426-1499). In contrast with his more innovative contemporaries Pollaiuolo and Verrocchio, Ghirlandaio employed throughout his career a somewhat conservative style of straightforward illustration which appealed to the more traditional tastes of the majority of Florentine patrons. Ghirlandaio and his workshop produced many large altarpieces, small devotional panels, and numerous portraits. In addition, he was responsible for most of the major frescos painted in Florence in the last quarter of the fifteenth century.

The Coronation of the Virgin with St. Justus of Volterra, the Blessed Jacopo Guidi of Volterra, St. Romuald, St. Clemens, and a Camaldolese Monk (63.1)

Tempera with oil on canvas, *270 x 176 (106 x 69).*

Provenance
Badia of San Giusto and San Clemente, Volterra.
San Salvatore, Volterra, as of 1650.
Collection of Cavaliere Toscanelli, Pisa, c. 1880.
Toscanelli Sale, Florence, Galleria Sambon, 9-23 April 1883.
Collection of Baron von Anrep, Ringen, Latvia.
Basel, Öffentliche Kunstsammlungen (on loan)
c. 1908-1936.
Schneeli Collection, Vuippens, Fribourg, Switzerland,
c. 1936.
Bass Collection, before 1963.

References
J.A. Crowe and G.B. Cavalcaselle, *A New History of Painting in Italy,* London 1864, vol. II, p. 425 (in the manner of Botticelli).
G. Vasari, *Le vite de' più eccellenti pittori, scultori e architetti, ed.* G. Malanesi, Florence 1878, vol. III, pp. 273, 318, n. 3.
A. Cinci, "La Badia dei Camaldolesi" in *Dall'archivo di Volterra. Memorie e documenti,* Volterra 1885, p. 9 (Ghirlandaio).

H. Ulman, *Sandro Botticelli,* Munich 1893, p. 75 (shop of Botticelli).
C. Ricci, *Volterra,* Bergamo 1905, pp. 82, 120 (school of Botticelli).
Katalog der öffentlichen Kunstsammlung in Basel, Basel 1908, p. 48, no. 213 (Florentine school, after 1470).
J.A. Crowe and G.B. Cavalcaselle, *A History of Painting in Italy,* London 1911, vol. IV, p. 262 (school of Botticelli).
C. Gamba, *Botticelli,* Milan 1936, pp. 208-9 (follower of Botticelli).
B. Berenson, *Italian Pictures of the Renaissance. Florentine School,* London 1963, vol. I, p. 37 (Botticelli, perhaps with the participation of Bartolomeo di Giovanni).
G. Mandel, *L'opera completa di Botticelli,* Milan 1967, no. 100 (shop of Botticelli).
B. Frederickson and F. Zeri, *Census of Pre-Nineteenth Century Italian Paintings in North American Public Collections,* Cambridge, Mass. 1972, pp. 34, 82 (Botticelli and Ghirlandaio).
Bass Catalogue 1973, No. 1 (Botticelli and Ghirlandaio).
R. Lightbown, *Botticelli,* London 1978, vol. II, pp. 143-44 (Botticelli and Ghirlandaio with assistants).

BOTTICELLI/GHIRLANDAIO

The Bass *Coronation of the Virgin* is one of the two altarpieces originally in the Camaldolese Badia of San Giusto e San Clemente, Volterra, described by Vasari in his *Life of Ghirlandaio* (see ref. Vasari). The two standing figures, Sts. Justus and Clemens, were the patron saints of the two churches of San Giusto and San Clemente in the precinct of the Badia of Volterra. St. Justus, wearing bishop's robes, and his brother Clemens, dressed as a magistrate, were the co-patrons of the city of Volterra. The figure kneeling on the left is St. Romuald, the patron saint of the Camaldolese order. The saint kneeling on the right is the Beato Jacopo Guidi da Certaldo (d. 1292), abbot of San Giusto and San Clemente, who was the object of a local cult in Volterra. His relics were housed in San Giusto together with those of Sts. Justus and Clemens (see ref. Lightbown). The donor of the work, the Camaldolese monk depicted in the lower right-hand corner, has not been identified.

Modern scholarship has judiciously rejected the traditional attribution of the Bass *Coronation* to Ghirlandaio in favor of a joint authorship by Ghirlandaio and Botticelli (see refs. Fredericksen & Zeri, Lightbown). The design of the lower half of the painting is very similar to the composition of the bottom portion of Ghirlandaio's other altarpiece for the Badia of Volterra, *Christ in Glory with St. Benedict, St. Actinia, St. Greciana, St. Romuald, and the Donor Abbot Giusto de' Bonvicini* (Volterra, Pinacoteca Comunale) of 1492. However, the design of the upper half of the painting, including the actual Coronation and the three angels dressed in green, red, and white, is not in keeping with Ghirlandaio's style of composition (cf. his *Coronation of the Virgin,* Narni, Municipio, of 1486), but it is chracteristic of the work of Botticelli. It specifically recalls Botticelli's *Coronation of the Virgin* (Florence, Uffizi) of c. 1490, formerly in San Marco, Florence. The figures of Mary and God the Father, who blesses her as he bestows the crown of immortality, are identical in both works; they have their ultimate source in Fra Filippo Lippi's fresco of the *Coronation of the Virgin* in the apse of the Cathedral of Spoleto of c. 1466-1469. A drawing of these two figures surrounded by angels (Göttingen, University Museum, 577B), attributed to the workshop of Botticelli by Berenson, has been connected with the San Marco *Coronation,* but it is more likely related to the Bass altarpiece.[1] The configuration of the angels in the drawing and their attributes are more similar to what is found in the later painting than in the earlier one.

The subject matter of the Bass painting, the Coronation of the Virgin, was a popular image in Italian medieval and Renaissance art. The essential elements of the composition—the figures of Mary and Christ or God the Father enthroned in Heaven, the music-making angels who welcome their Queen, and the saints who witness the event on earth—were established features of the iconography of the Coronation as of the late thirteenth century. The only major innovation in the representation of the scene occurred in the second half of the fifteenth century with the introduction of a panoramic landscape.[2] Among the earliest surviving examples of the new treatment are Piero Pollaiuolo's *Coronation of the Virgin,* signed and dated 1483, painted for the church of Sant' Agostino, San Gimignano, and Botticelli's own San Marco *Coronation* of c. 1490. The overall composition of the Bass altarpiece is in keeping with his late fifteenth-century formula.

Without precedent in the representation of the Coronation of the Virgin are the three large angels dressed in green, white, and red who represent the cardinal virtues of Faith, Hope, and Charity, respectively. In Christian thought, these are the three essential virtues in one's spiritual life that unite the worshipper to God (I Thess. 1:3, 5:B; I Cor. 13:13). According to Bartolomeo della Fonte, a Florentine theologian who wrote about the sacrament of penance c. 1468/69 in a book dedicated to Giuliano de' Medici, it is from faith, hope, and charity that love of divine virtue grows; this love leads in turn to penance, and ultimately to eternal beatitude.[3] In the context of the Coronation of the Virgin, the presence of the angelic personifications of Faith, Hope, and Charity in the Bass painting serve to involve the worshipper more intimately in the event, to move him to thought and prayers for his own salvation. The message is emphasized pictorially in the altarpiece in three ways: by the location of the three angels in the center of the painting, between the heavenly and terrestrial realms; by the reverent postures and gestures of the saints and the donor; and by the engaging glance of Beato Jacopo Guidi da Certaldo, who looks out of the painting.

Ghirlandaio and Botticelli collaborated on a number of occasions in the course of their careers. In 1480, in the church of the Ognissanti, Florence, they painted frescos of St. Augustine and St. Jerome respectively, in competition with one another. In 1480/81, the two artists were part of the team of painters who participated in the decoration of the Sistine Chapel. In 1482, they were commissioned jointly to decorate the Sala dei Gigli in the Palazzo Vecchio, Florence. (Botticelli's frescos have not survived.) In 1491, Botticelli, Ghirlandaio, and his brothers, were asked to provide designs for the mosaics of the Capella Maggiore of Florence Cathedral (the commission was never fulfilled). In the same year, Botticelli and Ghirlandaio worked together on frescos for Lorenzo il Magnifico in his (now destroyed) villa at Spedaletto, near Volterra. The Bass *Coronation of the Virgin,* which may be dated c. 1492 on the basis of stylistic and circumstantial evidence — the artists' joint residence near Volterra in that year — represents Botticelli's and Ghirlandaio's only known collaboratively produced panel painting and the only surviving example of their shared participation in the design and execution of a single composition. The Bass altarpiece is also important as the last major work of Ghirlandaio's career.

P.L.R.

1. B. Berenson, *The Drawings of the Florentine Painters,* Chicago 1938 [reprinted 1973], vol. 2, p. 60, fig. 208.
2. M. Echols, *The Coronation of the Virgin in Fifteenth Century Italian Art,* PhD. Dissertation, University of Virginia 1976, p. 208.
3. C. Trinkhaus, *In our Likeness—Humanity and Divinity in Italian Humanist Thought,* London 1970, vol. I, p. 629.

Condition: The support was transferred from the panel to canvas at some undetermined point in the past, with many associated losses. In the 1860s the painting was reported as being in a bad state (see ref. Cinci). Restored c. 1956/57, the work has been almost completely overpainted, but the underpainting is intact and the surface still conveys the character of the original inspired brushwork. Late eighteenth-century Italian frame, poplar.

SANDRO BOTTICELLI, Workshop

Italian, 1444-1510

Botticelli maintained a large workshop from the beginning of his career (c. 1470), but among his many pupils and assistants only one—Filippino Lippi (1457-1504)—became an independent artist in his own right. The role of Botticelli's shop in the production of artworks was not primarily to assist the master in the execution of his commissions but to provide copies and variations of his paintings at lower prices than those charged for autograph works. The demand for such workshop copies increased significantly in the 1480s as Botticelli's reputation grew.

The Mystic Marriage of St. Catherine (68.100)

Tempera on panel, *73.5 x 49 (20 x 19).*

Provenance

Collection Ferdinand von Quast, Radensleben, Ruppin, c. 1914.
Bass Collection, before 1963.

References

Die Kunstdenkmäler der Provinz Brandenburg, 1914, vol. I, p. 197, pl. 183 (Botticelli).
B. Berenson, *Italian Pictures of the Renaissance, Florentine School,* London 1963, vol. I, p. 37 (attributed to Bartolommeo di Giovanni).
Bass Catalogue 1973.
R. Lightbown, *Botticelli,* London 1978, vol. 2, p. 85 (workshop of Botticelli).

The Bass *Mystic Marriage of St. Catherine* is a typical product of Botticelli's shop, dating from the period 1490-1495. The composition—consisting of a kneeling figure of St. Catherine receiving a ring from the Christ Child seated in his mother's lap—is a copy with variations of an autograph work by Botticelli. The figures of the Madonna and Child replicate those in Botticelli's *Virgin and Child with St. John the Baptist,* (c. 1490-1495; New York, collection of Winthrop Rockefeller; see ref. Lightbown). They certainly rely on a drawing by the master kept in the shop (the same figures also appear in another workshop piece of c. 1490-1495, the *Adoration of the Magi,* Berlin,

Simon Collection). In contrast, the anatomical and proportional peculiarities of St. Catherine suggest that the figure was not derived directly from a drawing by the master, but was instead adapted for its new context from a figure of Mary kneeling in adoration, such as found in Botticelli's *Virgin Adoring the Holy Child* of c. 1490 (Washington, D.C., National Gallery) or from a figure by Botticelli of the Virgin Annunciate.

It is interesting to note that the Bass painting is the only Mystic Marriage of St. Catherine produced by Botticelli's shop; there is none by the master himself. St. Catherine of Siena, who was canonized only in 1461 although her cult was much older, was not an especially popular saint in Florence. It is most likely that this unusual choice of subject matter was suggested by the patron and may have been commissioned as part of a dowry for a nun.

The painting has been ascribed in the past to Bartolommeo di Giovanni (Berenson); however there is no solid evidence to support the attribution.

P. L. R.

Condition: Overpainting and retouches in many areas of the surface.

19

CORNELIS CORNELISZ VAN HAARLEM

Dutch, 1562-1638

ornelis Cornelisz, called Cornelis van Haarlem, was born at Haarlem in 1562. After an early training in Amsterdam and Antwerp, he stayed in France from c. 1579 and there absorbed the mannerist style of the School of Fountainebleau. In 1583 he returned to Haarlem where he lived and worked to the end of his life. Cornelis was influenced by Bartholomeus Spranger, but from the 1590s he combined Spranger's extreme mannerism with the new classicizing trends introduced by Hendrick Goltzius on his return from Italy. Cornelis is reported to have founded an 'Academy' in 1593, together with Goltzius and Carel van Mander, but this seems to have been only an informal association of artists for the purpose of drawing 'from life.'[1] Cornelis painted religious and mythological subjects, as well as portraits. He is known as one of the leading exponents of the late Dutch mannerist style.

The Crucifixion Triptych (63.16)

Painted c. 1600.
Panel, *center 108 x 72.4 (42½ x 20½), each wing 108 x 29 (42½ x 11¾).*

Provenance
Lord Ribblesdale, London.
Sotheby's, London, Lady Laura Lovat Sale, 19 March 1947, No. 111.
Christie's, London, Pascoe Rutter Sale, 4 November 1949, No. 146.
W. van Wijngaarden, Dieren, 1950.
D. Katz, Dieren/Basel, 1952.
Galerie Fischer, Luzern, 29 November 1955, No. 2042.
L.A.S.J. Baron van der Feltz, Brummen, 1956.
D. Katz, Dieren/Basel, 1959.
Bass Collection, 1963.

References
P.J.J. van Thiel, Letter to John Bass, 2 January 1967.
Bass Catalogue 1973, No. 16.
Peter C. Sutton, *Dutch Art in America,* Grand Rapids 1986, p. 152, fig. 220.

Exhibitions
Sarasota, Ringling Museum, *Dutch Seventeenth Century Portraits, The Golden Age,* 1981, No. 26.

Altarpieces in the form of a triptych or polyptych had a long tradition in sixteenth-century northern painting. A triptych consisted of a central panel with the major scene, and two hinged 'wings' with scenes related to the central theme. These three paintings were seen only on special occasions when the wings were opened (fig. A). More usually the wings were closed displaying a painted scene on the back of each wing, or treating the two wings as the surface for one painting which would be partly hidden by the two central strips of the frames (fig. B). The subjects painted on the backs of the wings had an iconographic connection with the major theme on the central panel inside. In the case of the Bass triptych the combined wings depict the *Fall of Man,* which caused all mankind to be burdened with the guilt of original sin. When the wings are opened this scene disappears and the central panel reveals the redemption from original sin through Christ's sacrifice on the cross.

Cornelis had painted the *Fall of Man* a few years earlier in 1592. His painting (now in the Rijksmuseum, Amsterdam) is closely related to Dürer's engraving of 1504 (B.1). The Bass version is clearly connected with Cornelis's earlier interpretation of the theme, but the figures are less muscular; their graceful slenderness and the deeply serious expressions of their faces lend them a spiritualized quality not present in either Cornelis's own 1592 painting or in Dürer's print. Cornelis included some of the traditional symbols of sin and lust in the shape of snails and a toad. The lion next to Eve alludes to the 'choleric temperament' which was considered the source of her cruel cunning disposition. The lion replaces the cat in Cornelis's earlier version, another animal associated with the choleric 'humor.' The snake with a female head and torso is repeated from the 1592 version. The two tiny figures in the background behind Adam's figure seem to show the

Fig. A: Outer Wings Opened; *The Crucifixion Triptych*.

Fig. B: Outer Wings Closed; *Fall of Man*

couple shortly after the creation of Eve. In their state of innocence they are naked, without the fig leaves that mark the shame of the Fall.

With the wings fully opened, the Crucifixion scene unfolds its poignant mystery. Christ's radiant figure flanked by the two thieves dominates the scene. His face expresses a deep faith and devotion, transcending physical suffering and death. Equally the faces of the soldiers express wonder and emotion rather than cruelty. Even the lancebearer, astride a horse at the left of the cross, and one of the soldiers casting dice on the right below the cross, share this expression of awe. The sponge-bearer, seen from behind on the right, and the swooning Virgin supported by the holy women with St. John, standing, on the left, complete the symmetrically balanced composition. Cornelis observed the tradition by which the good persons are placed on the Savior's right (left to the beholder) and the evil ones on His left. The central scene is pictorially linked to the wings through the landscape background and the sky with its dramatic transition from bright daylight on the left to deep nocturnal gloom over the right portion. Here again

light, symbol of salvation, is on Christ's right, and dark (evil) on His left. In the far distance is the city of Jerusalem and the procession of people following Christ to the cross. The figures in the side panels are portraits of the donor's family, accompanied by their patron saints. The male persons on the left wing are protected by St. James, who puts his arm around the older man. St. James was a fisherman and is identified by the sea shells on his cloak. The female members of the family are presided over by St. Apollonia, who holds a torch and her attribute, a pair of pincers. The children kneel on cushions, and all the figures are seen in an attitude of devotion directed toward the figure of Christ in the central panel.

The coat-of-arms on the chest in the left panel has been identified as belonging jointly to the Van Egmond family (left part), and the Bouckhorst family (right part—see ref. van Thiel).

M.A.R.

1. Carel van Mander, *Het Schilder-Boeck*, 2nd ed., Haarlem 1618; appendix with life of Van Mander by an anonymous biographer.

Condition: Apart from three cracks in the center panel, and one crack in each of the side panels, the triptych is in excellent condition with no paint losses.

CARLO DOLCI, Manner of

Italian, 1616-1686

C arlo Dolci was born and worked in Florence. He painted mainly religious subjects, with a sentimental approach that does not always appeal to modern critics. He was also a portrait painter.

Madonna (79.218)

Probably painted in the eighteenth century.

Canvas, *84.6 x 75.6 (33 x 29½).*

Provenance
Kunsthandel Karl Löscher & Anton Jancsy, purchased 28 July 1966.

Reference
Bass Catalogue 1973, No. 218 (as unknown eighteenth-century master).

This painting was sometimes ascribed to 'School of Sassoferrato', but Michael Helston, National Gallery, London, suggested Carlo Dolci as the more likely source. Comparisons with works by Dolci confirm this suggestion. The folded hands, heavy veil, inclination of the head, and pose seem typical of Dolci. Most of Sassoferrato's half-length madonnas, by contrast, have hands touching with fingertips only. His colors are much clearer and brighter than Dolci's.

M.A.R.

Condition: The picture is very dark and in need of cleaning.

ANTHONY VAN DYCK, After

Flemish, 1599-1641

Born in Antwerp, where he was the pupil of Hendrick van Balen, Anthony van Dyck established himself independently by c. 1615. He worked with Rubens in 1620, but was in England later that year and in Italy c. 1621-1627. On returning to England in 1632, he entered the service of Charles I and was later knighted. He set a standard of portraiture for aristocratic sitters, based partly on the example of Rubens, partly on a study of Titian and the Venetians. His English style combines a new bright and delicate palette with an endless variety of graceful yet dignified poses. His influence on European portraiture was profound and lasted in England for nearly two centuries.

Frances Howard, Duchess of Lennox and Richmond (1577-1639). (63.38)

An inscription on a simulated plaque, lower right, reads: *Francis Howard, Dutches of Richmond and Lennox, Daughter to Thomas Lord Howard of Bindon, who was second Sonne to Thomas Duke of Norfolke whose Mother was the Lady Elizabeth Stafford Eldest Daughter to Edward Duke of Buckingham. Her Grace was borne the 27. of. July 1577. AETATIS SVAE: 57. A° 1633.*

Canvas, *203.2 x 121.2 (79¼ x 47¼).*

Provenance
Said to have come from the collection of Alexander, 6th Earl and 1st Duke of Fife (1849-1912). There is a Thos. Agnew & Sons label on the crossbar of the stretcher, but when or how it passed through their hands is not known.
Recorded in the Bass Collection in 1963.

References
M. L. Boyle, *Biographical Catalogue of the Portraits at Longleat in the County of Wilts, the seat of the Marquess of Bath,* London 1881, p. 53, no. 16.

Oliver Millar, *Abraham van Der Doort's Catalogue of the Collection of Charles I,* Walpole Society, vol. XXXVII, London 1960, p. 6. Sir Oliver has been most generous in providing additional information and comment for this entry.

Bass Catalogue 1973, No. 38 (as William Dobson).

Frances, daughter of Thomas Howard, 1st Viscount Howard of Bindon, married first, Henry Pranell (d. 1599), second, Edward Seymour, Earl of Hertford (1537-1621), as his third wife, and third, in 1621, Ludovic Stuart, 3rd Duke of Lennox and Richmond (1574-1624), also as his third wife. She died in 1639 and is buried beside her last husband in Westminster Abbey. The Duke was Steward of the Household to James I and was in line of succession to the Scottish throne. His white wand of office as Steward may be enclosed within the long black mourning case which the Duchess holds. The coronet on the table, which does not correspond precisely to a ducal coronet, and the piece of crested silver beside it, may refer to his royal Stuart connection, as may also the fact that the Duchess stands under a Canopy of State. She wears a miniature of the Duke on her bosom. Her kerchief is embroidered with her initials, *F.R.L.* When the Duke died she published in French and English a pamphlet entitled *The Funerall Teares.*

The three sons of the Duke by an earlier marriage were all painted by Van Dyck: Lord James Stuart who succeeded his father as Duke and as Lord Steward (in a portrait which is now a part of the Iveagh Bequest, Kenwood, London) and Lords John and Bernard, who were both killed in the Civil War (in a double portrait formerly in the Broadlands Collection and now in The National Gallery, London).

The original of this portrait of the Duchess is not known to have survived. It may have been that which belonged to Charles I and was recorded by Abraham van der Doort, Surveyor of the King's Pictures, in his catalogue of the Royal Collection, as hanging in the Bear Gallery at Whitehall Palace: "Done by Sir Anthony Vandike Item the picture of the Dutches of Richmond done at length in a carved guilded frame." At the dispersal of the Royal Collection during the Commonwealth it may have entered the collection of Cardinal Mazarin (d. 1661), who is known to have owned a portrait of the Duchess which cannot now be traced. The Bass version is one of several copies of studio quality which differ from each other in minor details. In some the Duchess wears over her heart a miniature of the Duke, as here, and in others a square patch where the miniature would have been. Recorded surviving versions, mostly traditionally regarded as by or after Van Dyck, are in the collections of the Marquess of Bath at Longleat (style of Van Dyck), of the Duke of Buccleuch at Drumlanrig (after Van Dyck), of the late Hon. Lady Ward (Daniel Mytens), and of Mr. L.G. Stopford Sackville at Drayton Manor. Another was sold by Fischer of Luzern in 1932. There is a half-length version at Ranger's House, Blackheath, London.

The convention to which the portrait belongs is somewhat old-fashioned and formal for 1633 and especially for Van Dyck. The hieratic pose of the Duchess

with her hand and kerchief posed stiffly above the table and with the inscribed tablet in the lower right-hand corner belongs to the tradition of Paul van Somer and Daniel Mytens, and it is understandable that the name of Mytens has been associated with the painting, as in the portrait formerly belonging to the late Hon. Lady Ward (see above) and a copy that was sold at Christie's, 17 May 1946, lot 55, as by Mytens. Van Dyck had always presented his sitters with an easy elegance and it is difficult to understand his reversion to an earlier and different type unless the Duchess had herself requested it, perhaps wishing for a traditional commemorative mourning portrait. She was painted in 1635 by Cornelius Johnson. The recent ascription of the Bass portrait to William Dobson (1611-1646) is very unlikely.

K.J.G.

Condition: The paint surface has been much retouched. Face and arms, previously cleaned, are in good condition.

ANTHONY VAN DYCK, Follower of

Henrietta Maria (1609-1669), Queen of England (63.36)

Inscribed on the lower left of inset oval:
W. Dobson. A recent cleaning revealed the full signature/inscription, which previously was read as: *V.D. . . .*

Canvas, *64.8 x 55.2 (25½ x 21¾).*

Provenance
Collection Princess Irene Wiszniewska, London.
Bass Collection, 1963.

References
Bass Catalogue 1973, No. 36 (as A. van Dyck, attr.).

Henrietta Maria, youngest daughter of Henry IV of France and Marie de' Medici, married Charles I of England in 1625, the year of his accession to the throne. After his execution in 1649 she lived in France but was in England again, from 1660 to 1665. Van Dyck made several fine portraits of her which were often used as patterns for portraits produced in his studio or by his imitators.

In 1637, Bernini made a marble bust of Charles I based on Van Dyck's painting which had been sent to him in Rome showing three heads of the King on one canvas. (The bust was destroyed in the fire at Whitehall Palace in 1698). In 1639, the Queen decided to commission from Bernini a companion bust of herself. Van Dyck painted three separate portraits, one full-face and two in profile, for this purpose, but they were never sent to Rome.[1] Although the Bass portrait does not relate specifically to any of these, it depends on their manner of presentation and is one of a number of similar portraits of the Queen produced in the studio or by later imitators. The quality of the painting does not suggest that it comes from the Van Dyck studio. In the dress and jewelry it relates to portraits of the same type in the Spencer Collection at Althorp and The Lothian Collection of Melbourne Hall, Derbyshire. It is extremely unlikely that the inscription is an original signature by William Dobson. It is known that in his early days he made copies from Van Dyck but the quality of the painting suggests a minor artist. Both Oliver Millar and Malcolm Rogers consider the painting too weak for Dobson.

K.J.G.

1. For an account of the commissioning of Van Dyck's portraits to be sent to Bernini see Oliver Millar, *Van Dyck in England,* catalogue of the exhibition at the National Portrait Gallery, London 1983, p. 94.

Condition: In fair condition.

ANTHONY VAN DYCK, Style of

Portrait of a Gentleman (67.97)

Canvas, *112 x 82 (57¼ x 42¼).*

Provenance
M. Rothchild, London.
Sackville Gallery, London, 1931.
Bass Collection, 1967.

References
Gustav Gluck, *Van Dyck,* Klassiker der Kunst, 2nd ed., Stuttgart, 1931, p. 272 (as Van Dyck).
Certificates by H. Zimmermann, 1953; Hermann Voss, 1957; Ludwig Baldass, 1957 (all confirming an attribution to Van Dyck).
Bass Catalogue 1973, No. 97 (as attr. to Anthony Van Dyck).

The portrait reflects the sombre manner of Van Dyck's second Antwerp period, 1628-1632. It seems to have been executed by a contemporary Flemish artist who closely emulated the style of Antwerp's most prominent portrait painter.

M.A.R.

Flemish School

Sixteenth century

Two wing panels for an altarpiece: The Archangel Michael {left} and St. Bartholomew {right} (63.19 {b})

Panel, *each 121.8 x 43.6 (47½ x 17).*

The wings were attached to the museum's *Holy Family* painting by Marcellus Koffermans (63.19 [a]) at an unknown date before 1924. However measurements and frames do not quite match the Koffermans painting, and the quality of paint and stylistic character are different. The hinges of the wings are modern, and there is no indication of earlier hinges provided for the Koffermans painting.

For **provenance** and **references** see Koffermans, *The Holy Family.*

The left wing depicts the Archangel Michael, in white robe and crimson mantle, crushing the devil underneath his feet and slaying him with a spear. The composition is based directly on Martin Schöngauer's engraving of the same subject.[1] Another version of this painting, on a much smaller scale (canvas, *69 x 38*), copies the Schöngauer engraving in reverse.[2]

The right wing, apparently painted by a different artist, shows the figure of St. Bartholomew, dressed in emerald green and crimson robes. He is holding a book in his left arm and a knife, symbol of his martyrdom, in his right hand.

The brown tonality of the two wing panels, particularly in the sky and landscape, differs from the pale blue-green and silvery hues in the Koffermans *Holy Family.*

M.A.R.

1. Julius Baum, *Martin Schöngauer,* Vienna 1948, no. 64.
2. Escorial, Chambers of the Infanta Isabella Clara. See Elisa Bermejo, "Dos Pinturas Ineditas en El Escorial" in *Real Monasterio-Palacio de El Escorial,* Madrid 1987, p. 249f.

Condition: The left panel is in better condition than the right. Both are partly covered in discolored varnish, particularly noticeable in the landscapes.

GOVERT FLINCK

Dutch, 1615-1660

Govert Flinck was born at Cleves and settled in Amsterdam in 1632. From 1632 to 1635 he studied with Rembrandt and for the next decade his work clearly shows Rembrandt's influence. From 1645 Flinck adopted the more popular, elegant manner of the fashionable portrait painter Bartholomeus van der Helst. His subsequent success overshadowed Rembrandt's. In 1659 Flinck was awarded the most important commission then available to a Dutch artist, for twelve large-scale paintings to decorate the new Town Hall of Amsterdam. He died before he could start this work, and the commission was divided among three artists, including Rembrandt who had previously been excluded.

Isaac Holding the Apple of Obedience (63.12)

Painted c. 1638-1645.

Inscribed in lower right corner with number *243,* in decorative writing which seems contemporary with the painting.

Canvas, *103.8 x 79.5 (40½ x 31).*

Provenance
Castle Ludwigsburg, Inventory dated 1767, No. 20 (as Rembrandt).
Staatsgalerie Stuttgart, from 1846, Inventory No. 446 (as Flinck).
Collection Kisters, Kreuzlingen, sold in 1958 (see ref. Moltke).
Collection Roeder.
Bass Collection, before 1963.

References
O. Eisenmann, "Zur Stuttgarter Gemäldegalerie," *Kunstchronik,* 23, 1887/88, p. 299.
Th. von Frimmel, *Blätter für Gemäldekunde,* vol. 3, 1907, p. 117.
Staatsgalerie Stuttgart, *Catalogue,* 1907, p. 267 (as school of Rembrandt); *Catalogue,* 1957, no. 446 (as G. Flinck).
J. W. von Moltke, *Govaert Flinck 1615-1660,* Amsterdam 1966, p. 152.
Bass Catalogue 1973, No. 12.
W. Sumowski, *Drawings of the Rembrandt School,* ed. W. Strauss, New York 1979, vol. I, p. 222, cat. 99 (as Ferdinand Bol).
Albert Blankert, *Ferdinand Bol (1616-1680), Rembrandt's Pupil,* Doornspijk 1982, cat. 137, p. 142, pl. 148 (as Ferdinand Bol).
Wayne Franits, "On the Subject Matter of Rembrandt's Etching, B33," *Marsyas, Studies in the History of Art,* 21, 1981-82, p. 13f., fig. 3. (as G. Flinck).
Peter C. Sutton, *Dutch Art in America,* Grand Rapids 1986, p. 153 (quoting Blankert's reattribution to F. Bol).

The painting must date from a period prior to 1645 when Flinck was closely following Rembrandt's style. The rich warm colors, soft chiaroscuro, and atmospheric handling are characteristic of the most successful works of the Rembrandt School. The canvas was at some time reduced in size, which affects the spatial balance of the composition.

The painting was previously entitled "Boy Offering An Apple". This title, though accurately describing what we see, does not clarify the content of the scene. The boy in the painting is not dressed in contemporary Dutch clothes but wears a long tasseled tunic, richly embroidered and bejeweled, over a white shirt with billowing sleeves. Around his neck hangs a heavy gold chain with a medallion and his head is covered with a soft velvet cap. The boy's attire is of the kind usually chosen by Rembrandt and other seventeenth-century artists for characters from the Old Testament.

Govert Flinck did, in fact, adopt the figure of the boy from an etching by his master, Rembrandt, entitled *Abraham Caressing His Son* (B.33; New York, Pierpont Morgan Library; see fig. 1). This etching, dating from 1638, shows a child dressed in the same clothes as the boy in the Bass picture. The boy in Rembrandt's etching holds out an apple towards the beholder, in a pose echoed by the child in the Bass picture.

The title given to Rembrandt's etching by his

Fig. 1: Rembrandt, *Abraham Caressing His Son Isaac.* Etching. New York, The Pierpont Morgan Library.

contemporaries has been questioned by twentieth-century art historians. However, recent research has proved it correct (see ref. Franits). In the sixteenth and seventeenth centuries the apple was a familiar symbol of a child's obedience to his parents, and Isaac, who willingly followed his father to the sacrifice, was regarded as the ideal obedient son, an example for children to follow. Isaac's obedience is being emphasized by both Rembrandt and Flinck with the attribute of the apple. The literature and folklore of the period frequently refer to this symbolism; Luther himself used it when commenting on Isaac's obedience to his father: "Thus a father takes an apple away from his boy... not because he wants to deprive him of it, but merely to make a test of whether his son loves him... If the son gives up the apple, the father is pleased with the son's obedience and love."[1] Children in sixteenth- and seventeenth-century Dutch portraiture are often shown holding an apple, symbol of their obedience to their parents. The symbolism survives to our own day in the idea of a child bringing to school an apple for the teacher.

Flinck seems to have based his composition on Rembrandt's preparatory drawing (now lost) rather than the etching. The pose of the boy in the drawing would have been identical to that in the painting, while in the print it is side-reversed.[2]

Albert Blankert (see ref.) attributes the Bass picture to another Rembrandt pupil, Ferdinand Bol, but Moltke and other scholars, e.g. Franits (see ref.) and Haverkamp-Begemann (verbal information) give it to Flinck. When the painting is studied in the original (which Blankert probably had no opportunity to do), the attribution to Flinck seems entirely convincing. Other earlier attributions include G. Horst and Aert de Gelder (see Stuttgart cats. 1907 and 1957).

M.A.R.

1. Luther, *Works*, St. Louis 1955-76, vol. IV, pp. 21-25, 131-32 (quoted by Franits).
2. Sumowski (see ref.) associated a drawing in the National Museum in Stockholm (Inv. No. 2010/1863), which he attributes to F. Bol, with the Bass painting. However, the relationship of the drawing and the painting is not very obvious.

Condition: The canvas appears to be cut on all four margins, with the edges left rough and uneven. This suggests that the present picture has been reduced from a larger composition.

FRENCH/SPANISH SCHOOL, Attributed to

Second half of the fifteenth century

Madonna of Humility (63.28)

Tempera on panel, *160x109 (64½ x 42½).*

Provenance
Collection Louis-Pierre Bresset, Marseilles, 1952.
Bass Collection, 1963.

References
Bass Catalogue 1973, No. 28 (as Aragonese school).
Prof. Judith Berg Sobré (University of Texas at San Antonio), Letters to the Bass Museum, 11 and 30 March 1987 (attribution uncertain).

Exhibitions
Marseilles, Musée Cantini, *L'Art du Moyen Age dans les collections Marseillaises,* May-July 1952, no. 21 (as Central France, fifteenth century).

The iconographic type of the Madonna of Humility first appeared in northern Italy during the fourteenth century. The title is derived from the Latin word *humus* (ground), for the Virgin is shown seated on the ground, sometimes on a cushion as in this panel. The saints in the six side panels have not been identified.

The painting is an example of the international gothic style, in which Italian and Northern trends mingle freely, so it is often difficult to determine a work's place of origin.

In the Bass Catalogue of 1973 the painting was attributed to the Aragonese School, fifteenth century. Previously, while in a French collection, it was ascribed to "Central France, fifteenth century" (see exhibition Marseilles). Recently, the attribution to the Aragonese School has been decisively rejected by Judith Berg Sobré (see ref.). Professor Sobré is also unconvinced of any Spanish origin, but she sees some slight connection with the Mallorcan painter Gabriel Moger (fl. 1414-1438). However, the style of the frame is too late for Moger's dates and the possibility of a French artist cannot be ruled out. The painting needs further research after a judicious cleaning.

M.A.R.

Condition: In spite of some cracks in the panel, with old fills and retouchings, the painting is in good condition and set in its original Gothic frame, considered Flemish or French by S. Robinson. Incised lines in the gesso ground do not always follow the design and may indicate the presence of *pentimenti,* such as changed positions of the figures and, possibly, additional angels which were not included in the final paint surface. Incised and punched haloes. The varnish applied after an old cleaning (with much overpainting) is now very dirty.

33

GERMAN SCHOOL

Last quarter of the sixteenth century

Duke Heinrich von Sachsen - Lauenburg (1550-1585), Archbishop of Bremen (79.185)

No signature or date. A Dürer monogram was once in the upper left corner, but has disappeared. There is an engraving after this portrait by Louis Lucas with the inscription: *Christopher Amberger pinx.*

Panel, *106.7 x 88.9 (42 x 35).*

Provenance
Prince Demidoff, San Donato.
Stanley Mortimer, New York, 1944.
Parke-Bernet, New York, 22 & 23 November 1963, No. 69.
Kunsthandel Xaver Scheidwimmer OHG, Munich.
Purchased 22 July 1966 for the Bass Collection.

References
L'Art, 1883, vol. II, facing page 60, reproduction of the engraving by Louis Lucas, with the title *Portrait d'un Gentilhomme Allemand, (Galérie de M. le prince Demidoff de San Donato à son chateau de Pratolino).*
Kurt Langenheim, "Erzbischof Heinrich III, Herzog von Sachsen-Lauenburg," *Lauenburgische Heimat,* N.F. 58, September 1967, p. 16f., ill. p. 17.
Bass Catalogue 1973, No. 185 (as Christoph Amberger).
Dr. Kurt Locher, Germanisches Nationalmuseum, Nürnberg, Letter dated 30 September 1986.

The picture has been attributed in the past to the German painter Christoph Amberger (c. 1505-1562). However, Amberger could not have painted this portrait, since the sitter was only twelve years old at the time of the painter's death. The portrait shows Heinrich von Sachsen-Lauenburg as a man aged about thirty, and thus must have been painted around 1580, when he had reached the peak of his power. The subject of portraiture in Germany during the second half of the sixteenth century has as yet hardly been investigated and the name of the artist remains unknown. Dr. Kurt Locher from the Germanisches National Museum, Nürnberg, suggests on stylistic grounds a connection with the Netherlands (see ref.). A German artist, possibly trained in the Netherlands, seems the most plausible attribution. The previous attribution to Amberger however is not without foundation, since the Bass painting does closely resemble in pose and composition some of Christoph Amberger's portraits, particularly that of *Jörg Hermann,* dated 1530, in the Galerie Harrach, Vienna. The painter of the Bass portrait clearly paid tribute to this earlier tradition.

The sitter's identity is securely established by the elaborate coat-of-arms in the upper right corner, which is fully analyzed in Kurt Langenheim's article (see ref.). The two red-and-gold striped shields of the Askanian House are joined by the three red crescents *(Seeblätter)* on white ground and the golden eagle in a blue field representing the regions Engern and Wuppertal in the coat-of-arms of the Dukes of Lauenburg. The red wheel in a white field stands for the bishopric Osnabrück, the crossed keys in a red field for the archbishopric of Bremen, and the red cross on white ground for the bishopric of Paderborn. Heinrich, third son of Duke Franz I of Sachsen-Lauenburg, was made Archbishop of Bremen in 1567 and Bishop of Osnabrück in 1574. In 1579 he also became the administrator of the bishopric of Paderborn. The coat-of-arms accurately 'lists' all his worldly and ecclesiastical honors. It is topped with three helmets, two crowns, an Elector's hat, sword and crosier and other emblems relating to the archbishop's office and status.

Heinrich is wearing the characteristic 'Spanish Court Costume', consisting of a black silk doublet with white ruff under an ample fur-lined cloak.[1] A black hat with plume and jewelled band and a large gold chain complete the costume. The rich jewelry worn by the archbishop further enhances his status. On the gold chain around his neck hangs a toothpick made of gold and jewels. This kind of toothpick worn on a chain was common all over Europe from at least the fourteenth century. Attached to it are a gold-ornamented cylindrical container and another very small elongated vessel, both used for perfume or medicine. A heavy gold signet ring supported by a 'guard-ring' is worn on the index finger, and three narrow heavily bejewelled gold rings adorn the small finger of the left hand. The gold or silver hatband, set with pearls, was common for princes from the fifteenth century onwards.[2]

Heinrich was married to Anna Broich from Cologne. There were no children. He was killed in a riding accident in 1585 when he was only thirty five.

A photo-replica on canvas of this portrait in original size is on display in the permanent historical collection of the Kreismuseum of the Kreis Herzogtum Lauenburg, Ratzeburg, Germany.

M.A.R.

1. The ruff is characteristic of the type worn c. 1570-1580. Ruffs made their first appearance in 1555 but initially they were no more than a narrow finely pleated band on a very high collar. The archbishop's ruff is an intermediary form. Towards the end of the century ruffs became generally fuller and more prominent.
2. Information on the jewelry was kindly offered (verbally) by R. Lightbown, curator of the Jewelry Department, Victoria & Albert Museum, London.

Condition: The paint surface has suffered, particularly in the areas of the fur, apparently from overcleaning.

GERMAN SCHOOL

c. 1600

The Kiss of Judas (63.30)

Copper, *39 x 29 (14½ x 10¾).*

Attached to the verso is a print of Albrecht Dürer's woodcut *The Kiss of Judas* (Hollstein No. 116), which served as a model for the painting. The print, attached with rabbit-hair glue, seems to have been in its position a long time, perhaps from shortly after the painting was finished.

The cassetta type frame is typical of the period and of outstanding quality; it could be the primary frame for this painting. It is made mainly of oak, with walnut burl panels in the center. The moldings have been regilded.

Provenance
Bass Collection, 1963.

References
Bass Catalogue 1973, No. 30 (as attributed to the Master of Messkirch).
Thomas DaCosta Kaufmann, Letter to the Bass Museum, 9 December 1986 (Germany, c. 1600).

The subject of the painting is one of the scenes of the Passion, when Judas, with a kiss, betrays Christ to the Israelite soldiers who bind him and lead him away to the High Priest for judgment.

The painter followed closely the composition of Dürer's woodcut, taken from the 'Grand Passion' series, but his brightly lit forms stand out with great plasticity against the gloom of the nocturnal scene. The light has a supernatural quality and adds a sense of foreboding as it strikes the spectral shape of the gnarled tree in the upper right and the tortured spikes of the dead tree. The flickering torches and the effect of lightning in the sky add to the dramatic tension. The painter also individualized the features of the participating characters, imbuing the face of Christ with a moving nobility. The painter was a sensitive artist who reinterpreted Dürer's work rather than merely copying it.

The name of the artist remains unknown. The picture was previously attributed to the Master of Messkirch (active c. 1500-1543), but it belongs to a later period. Its style and character suggest the School of Prague in the late sixteenth century, when Rudolph II inspired a Dürer revival that spread over many parts of northern Europe. The Emperor's love for the German masters of an earlier generation, and particularly for Dürer, was legendary.[1] He had Dürer's famous painting of the *Madonna of the Rosary* brought from its church in Venice to Prague, where it remains to the present day. His collection was full of works of the old masters, including Italians. Works he could not acquire he had copied by his court painters.[2]

The style of the Bass painting does not point to any particular painter at the court of Prague, but it was conceived and executed in the spirit of admiration for Dürer that found its expression in many copies and free adaptations of the great German master's work made around the turn of the sixteenth century.

M.A.R.

1. For the history of the Dürer revival, see T. DaCosta Kaufmann, *L'École de Prague,* Paris 1985, p. 68f.
2. Ibid., p. 69.

Condition: In good condition.

DER MEISTER VON MESSKIRCH

DOMENICO GHIRLANDAIO, Workshop

Italian, 1449-1494

Domenico Ghirlandaio headed a large shop in which he was assisted by his two brothers Benedetto (1458-1497) and Davide Bigordi (1452-1525). Among his many pupils were his brother-in-law Sebastiano Mainardi (active 1493-1513), Francesco Granacci (1469-1543), and for a short while in the late 1480s the young Michelangelo. Although the output of Ghirlandaio's shop was enormous, the works produced were relatively uniform in design and execution. It has therefore proved difficult to identify or evaluate the extent of the contributions of his brothers and of other assistants in the production of specific works.

The Madonna Adoring the Christ Child with Angels and the Infant St. John the Baptist (63.25)

Oil with tempera, wooden tondo, *diameter 94.8 (37)*.

Provenance
Christie's, London, Howorth Sale, 14 December 1923.
Bass Collection, before 1963.

Reference
Bass Catalogue 1973, No. 25 (attributed to Sebastiano Mainardi).

The Bass tondo has been attributed in the past to Sebastiano Mainardi. Although there are works ascribed to Mainardi which are similar in style, as yet his autograph oeuvre has not been well-defined. It is therefore methodologically unsound in view of the current state of scholarship to assign the Bass painting to him.

The Bass tondo is one of the many Adorations produced by Ghirlandaio and his shop. The figures of the Madonna and Child repeat, in reverse, those found in one of Ghirlandaio's most outstanding works, the altarpiece of the *Adoration of the Shepherds,* painted c. 1485 for the Sassetti Chapel in Santa Trinità, Florence. The background landscape, the ruined wall, and the figures of the angels have parallels in other paintings by the master, such as the *Adoration of the Magi* (Ospedale degli Innocenti, Florence) of 1488.

The subject matter of the Madonna adoring the Christ Child in a landscape surrounded by saints and angels was one of the most common devotional images of late fifteenth-century Florentine painting. It was introduced into Renaissance art by Fra Filippo Lippi in the 1460s in a series of three paintings—*The Madonna Adoring the Christ Child* (Berlin, Dahlem Museum), painted for the altar of the chapel in the Medici Palace; *The Madonna Adoring the Christ Child* (Florence, Uffizi), painted for the penitential cell at the monastery of Camaldoli belonging to Lucrezia Tornabuoni, the wife of Piero de' Medici; and *The Madonna Adoring the Christ Child with St. Hilarion*

(Florence, Uffizi). The Bass tondo shares a number of symbolic features with these earlier versions.[1] The Christ Child is shown pointing to His mouth with one finger, thereby identifying Himself as the 'Word' (John 1:14) and emphasizing His humanity. John the Baptist holds a banderole conspicuously inscribed with the word "Ecce," which is the beginning of the phrase "Ecce agnus Dei," pronounced by the adult Baptist when he baptized Christ (John 1:29). John the Baptist's presence thus emphasizes the divinity of Christ and points to His future sacrifice. The flowery field in which the Virgin kneels and the Christ Child rests may be understood symbolically as the new garden of Eden in which the new Eve (Mary) adores the new Adam (Christ). The fragmentary wall, dividing the foreground occupied by the figures from the background, surely alludes to the old order which came to an end with the advent of the new era of grace under Christ. Finally, the landscape of rocks and a distant seashore—which is not found in Lippi's paintings of the Adoration but which was a common setting for many Renaissance paintings of the Madonna—also has symbolic significance. The seashore is a reference to Mary's title in her litany, the "Star of the Sea and the Port of our Salvation." Her symbol, the star (of the sea), is also embroidered in gold on the left shoulder of her dark mantle. The rocks probably refer to Christ, and specifically allude to Daniel's prophecy of the Virgin Birth (Daniel 2:33-36). Daniel, in a vision, saw a stone cut without hands, which fell from a mountain, smashed the idol with the feet of clay, and then grew to become a mountain which filled the entire earth.

P.L.R.

1. A free version of this tondo, by a different hand, is in the Musée d'Art et d'Histoire in Geneva (inv. no. 1975-39), there attributed to an unknown artist close to Rosselli and Ghirlandaio.

Condition: The tondo support is cradled on the back and has been shaved down. Much of the painting is overpainted with glazes or retouches, but major passages are intact and in good condition.

EL GRECO (DOMINIKOS THEOTOKOPULOS), Studio of

Spanish (born Greek), 1541-1614

The artist known as El Greco (the Greek) was born in Crete and, after an early training in the late Byzantine style of Crete, he traveled to Venice where he was influenced by the work of Titian and Tintoretto. In 1570 he was in Rome and there fell under the spell of Michelangelo. Then, from 1577 until his death, El Greco lived and worked in Toledo, Spain, where he developed his intensely emotional, spiritualized manner of painting. His unnaturally elongated figures, apparently weightless and boneless, are symbols of ecstatic religious devotion. However El Greco also painted a number of admirable portraits (e.g. *Cardinal Guevara,* New York, Metropolitan Museum of Art) and two famous landscapes of Toledo. El Greco's art perfectly expressed the religious fervor of his adopted city, where he was constantly in demand for altarpieces and paintings of saints and biblical subjects.

St. Francis Standing in Meditation (63.5)

Painted after 1595.

Canvas, *64.7 x 51.3 (25¼ x 20).*

Provenance
Collection Franz von Segesser, Luzern.
Bass Collection, 1963.

References
Dr. Herman Voss, Certificate, Munich, 20 August, 1959 (as original work by El Greco).
Bass Catalogue 1973, No. 5 (as attributed to El Greco).
Edward J. Sullivan, Letter to the Bass Museum, 25 March 1986, with appendix.

The Bass picture shows St. Francis of Assisi, one of the most popular saints in Spain and Italy, in the traditional pose of penitence and meditation. Standing in front of a cavern, he meditates upon a skull (symbol of human mortality) and upon the crucifix (symbol of man's eternal salvation through Christ). A vine at the upper left is symbolic of the resurrection. The placement of these symbolic motifs has been carefully thought out by the artist. From the upturned palm of the saint's left hand, the composition flows up to the skull (mortality), through Christ (salvation) to the vine (immortality).

El Greco, a secular Franciscan, created thirteen different variants of the figure of St. Francis, and numerous replicas were produced by the workshop. The quality of the Bass painting suggests that it was done, probably in the studio, by an artist close to El Greco (see ref. Sullivan), based on the signed painting now in the Torello Collection, Barcelona. Another signed version is in the Joslyn Art Museum, Omaha,[1] but this version differs from the Torello painting and the Bass replica in various nuances: for instance, the discrepancy in the sizes of the saint's right and left hands is greater in the Joslyn version, where the left hand is also anatomically more distorted.

M.A.R.

1. For an account of the Omaha and Barcelona versions of *Saint Francis Standing in Meditation,* see Harold E. Wethey, *El Greco and His School,* Princeton 1962, vol. 2, pp. 222-23.

Condition: In fair condition.

40

41

JOHN HOPPNER, R.A.

British, 1758-1810

Hoppner was a successful but very uneven portrait painter whose reputation has fluctuated considerably in this century. He studied at the Royal Academy schools and initially modelled his style almost exclusively on that of Reynolds. He was appointed Portrait Painter to the Prince of Wales in 1789, was elected A.R.A. in 1793 and R.A. in 1795. His confidence and, in consequence, his standard of achievement were undermined by the phenomenal early success of Thomas Lawrence who was eleven years his junior.

Lucius Concannon, Esq., M.P. (79.321)

Canvas, *126.9 x 102.5 (49½ x 40).*

Provenance

Christie's Sale, 8 May, 1908, lot 118.
Viscount Leverhulme Sale, Anderson Galleries, New York,
17-19 February 1926, lot 148, bought by the Ehrich
Gallery.
Blumenthal Estate.
Bass Museum, 1979.

References

W. McKay and W. Roberts, *John Hoppner,* London 1909,
p. 54.
American Art Annual, 1926, p. 409.
Bass Catalogue 1973, No. 321.

There has been some confusion as to the identity of this sitter. The portrait seems to have been engraved twice, once by J. Ward and once by J. Murphy, both engravings being untitled and undated. The sitter has sometimes been thought to be George Hibbert of the East India Company, but Hibbert was born in 1757 and the portrait of him painted by Lawrence in 1800 shows no resemblance at all to the sitter in the Bass painting. The identification by W. McKay and W. Roberts as Lucius Concannon may be accepted (see ref.). The portrait is a straightforward example of Hoppner's middle-of-the-road style. In this case he seems to have taken his cue from Romney rather than from Reynolds. McKay and Roberts tentatively date Murphy's engraving to c. 1795-1805 which would seem to be the probable date of the painting.

Details of the life of Lucius Concannon are elusive. He was, presumably, a member of one of the Irish landed families of that name. The *Eton College Register* states that he was probably, but not certainly, the boy of the name of Concannon or Cancanen who was a pupil there from 1779 to 1783. We know, also from the *Eton College Register,* that he was a Member of Parliament for Appleby, 1818-1820, and Winchelsea, 1820-1823, and that he died in 1823. There is however no obituary notice in *The Gentleman's Magazine* which is where one would expect to find one.

Condition: Restored in 1984, when two accidental punctures were repaired.

Jane, Countess of Oxford, with Her Daughter (63.33)

Canvas, *224.3 x 146.2 (87½ x 57)*.

A typed note attached to the back is an extract from a letter from Mr. Lockett Agnew (43, Old Bond Street, London W) to the Dowager Lady Burton, 10 July 1913:
Dear Lady Burton.

You asked me my opinion of the picture. It is a perfectly beautiful picture by Hoppner; I do not think (except "The Frankland Children" and the Celebrated picture of "Miranda") that I have ever seen a picture by this artist so elegant and so attractive; it is more like "Sir Joshua" in his finest manner.

You say in a former letter that when I see this picture, I will like to keep it. Most certainly I should like to keep it and should like to send you a cheque for L 2 {indecipherable digit} 000 for this picture.
Yours sincerely
{Signed} Lockett Agnew.

Another label on the back reads:
Mar 17{5}8
In dining room
J. Hoppner, R.A.
Countess of Oxford & Child
Canvas 92 x 57 inch.

Provenance
Probably passed from Lady Langdale (d. 1873) to Mrs. Harley, Brampton Brian, Herefordshire.
Lord Burton at Rangemore Hall, Burton-on-Trent, 1909.
Christie's sale, 27 May, 1959, lot 79.
Bass Museum, 1963.

References
W. McKay and W. Roberts, *John Hoppner,* London 1909, p. 192.
The Farington Diary, ed. J. Grieg, vol. II, 1923, p. 36.
Bass Catalogue 1973, No. 33 (attributed to Hoppner).

Exhibitions
Royal Academy, 1797, No. 167.

This portrait was exhibited at the Royal Academy in 1797. It shows Hoppner at his most derivative in that he clearly had the example of Reynolds in his mind from the beginning. The uncomfortable elongation of Lady Oxford's right thigh derives from such Reynolds compositions as *Lady Sarah Bunbury Sacrificing to the Graces* (Art Institute, Chicago) or *Mrs. Lloyd* (private collection, England), where Reynolds is consciously making use of a stylization that is found in Italian mannerist painting, especially in the work of Parmigianino.

Jane Elizabeth (1774-1824), daughter of the Rev. James Scott, Vicar of Itchen, Hampshire, married Edward Harley, 5th Earl of Oxford, in 1794. Their eldest daughter, also named Jane Elizabeth, who is shown here with her mother, was born in 1796. In 1835 she married Henry Bickersteth, later Master of the Rolls, who was created Baron Langdale in 1851.

Lady Oxford was a noted beauty. She was sociable and impulsive. Her marriage was unsatisfactory and she gained a certain notoriety when, during a visit to Paris in 1802 after the Peace of Amiens, she was much seen in company with Arthur O'Connor, an Irish political rebel. Later her name was frequently associated with Lord Byron. Sir Uvedale Price wrote to Samuel Rogers in 1824, "Had she been united to a man she loved, esteemed and respected, she herself might have been generally respected and esteemed, as well as loved; but in her situation, to keep clear of all misconduct, required a strong mind or a cold heart; perhaps both, and she had neither.... There was something about her, in spite of her errors, remarkably attaching, and that something was not merely her beauty". At the Royal Academy exhibition of 1798, Hoppner showed a second portrait of Lady Oxford, a half-length, which became one of his best-known and most popular works. It was bequeathed by Lady Langdale to the National Gallery, London.

K.J.G.

Condition: In fair condition.

ITALIAN SCHOOL (Lombard), Attributed to

Seventeenth century

Portrait of a Young Girl as Venus (79.236)

Canvas, *84.6 x 62.8 (33 x 24½).*

Inscribed on a Cartellino: *MOSTRA CON LA BELTA*
GRATIE ET AMORI
MA CON TURCO RIGOR
SAETTA I CORI
Anno aetatis suae XV

Inscribed on gummed labels on reverse: lower left,
I-670, upper right, *8961.* The inscription on the lower left
label may indicate a date of 1670.

Provenance
L'Etagère, Antiquities, Paris 1966.
Bass Collection

References
Bass Catalogue 1973, No. 236 (as unknown seventeenth-
century Italian master).

The painting shows a young lady wearing a sumptuous
dress, rich jewelry and a decorative turban. She is
attended by the winged and blindfolded figure of Cupid
who holds his bow in his left hand.

On a *cartellino* held by Cupid and the girl, her age is
given as fifteen; the inscribed stanza pays tribute to her
beauty and grace but warns that her arrows will deeply
pierce hearts. She is holding one of Cupid's arrows in her
right hand, ready to fulfill this promise.

The attribution to the Lombard School was suggested
by Sir Michael Levey who saw a photograph of the
painting. Another suggestion (by the late Sir Geoffrey
Agnew) was Angelo Caroselli (1585-1627), a Roman
painter. The Neapolitan school has been suggested on
various occasions. The *Portrait of a Girl (15 x 11),* described
as Neopolitan School and recorded in the Witt Library,
London, as being in the R. Draper Collection, Miami,
bears a resemblance to the Bass painting, but the collection
cannot be traced.

M.A.R.

Condition: Fair Condition.

JACOB JORDAENS

Flemish, 1593-1678

Jacob Jordaens spent his life in his native city, Antwerp, where he was the pupil and son-in-law of Adam van Noort, one of Rubens's teachers. Like other painters of his generation, Jordaens was strongly influenced by Rubens, whose fame dominated the artistic scene of Europe in the first half of the seventeenth century. Like Rubens, Jordaens painted religious and mythological subjects, often on large-scale canvases, and he was also an excellent portraitist. His manner lacks the refinement of Rubens, but shows a characteristic baroque vigor and coloristic exuberance. After the death of Rubens in 1640, Jordaens became the most sought-after 'history painter' in northern Europe. He was called in to contribute to the decorations of the Huis ten Bosch at the Hague, and with other artists, including Rembrandt, to make paintings for the new Town Hall in Amsterdam in 1660.

Nymphs and Satyrs (Allegory of Fruitfulness) (79.275)

Painted c. 1615.

Panel, *64.1 x 78.2 (25 x 30½).*

Provenance

Collection Meyer, Minden.
Bartels, Minden/Berlin, 1869, Sale to Grossherzogliche Gemäldegalerie, Oldenburg (No. 125).
Dr. Hans Tietje, Amsterdam, from before 1929 to after 1933.
Galerie Fischer, Luzern.
Sold to John Bass, 5 Dec. 1968.

References

Wilhelm Bode, *Die Grossherzogliche Gemälde-Galerie zu Oldenburg,* Wien 1888, p. 72f. (Rubens).
Max Rooses, *L'Oeuvre de P.P. Rubens,* Antwerp 1890, vol. III, p. 133, no. 653; vol. V, pp. 339-40.
Adolf Rosenberg, *Rubens,* Klassiker der Kunst, Stuttgart 1905, p. 90.
A. Bredius, *Die Grossherzogliche Gemäldegalerie zu Oldenburg,* Oldenburg 1906, p. 24.
R. Oldenbourg, *P. P. Rubens,* Klassiker der Kunst, Stuttgart 1921, pp. 60, 457 n. (doubts the attribution to Rubens, suggesting P. Soutman as possible alternative).
Gustav Glück, *Rubens, Van Dyck und ihr Kreis,* Vienna 1933, Nachträge, p. 371f. (comment by L. Burchard, p. 392: "nothing to do with Rubens").
Bass Catalogue 1973, no. 275 (as Rubens).
R.A. d'Hulst, *Jacob Jordaens,* tr. P. S. Falla, London 1982, pp. 55, 75, 330 n. 19; fig. 22.
Julius S. Held, Letter to the Bass Museum, 11 November 1985.

Exhibitions

Düsseldorf, Kunstverein, *Ausstellung alter Malerei aus Privatbesitz,* 1929, no. 54 (as Rubens).
Amsterdam, J. Goudstikker, *Rubens-Tentoonstelling,* 1933, no. 35 (as Rubens).

The attribution of this painting has been controversial. With only two exceptions, all sources, up to and including the 1973 Bass Catalogue, attributed it to Rubens, the exceptions being R. Oldenbourg in Klassiker der Kunst, suggesting in a footnote an alternative attribution to Soutman, and L. Burchard (see ref. Glück), stating categorically that the painting "has nothing to do with Rubens". In recent years the attribution to Rubens has been rejected and the picture has been listed in the museum's files as "in the manner of Rubens". Julius Held (1985) judged that it was "obviously done by an artist very much under Rubens' influence". Other scholars, e.g. E. Haverkamp Begemann (1986, verbal information) shared this opinion. R. A. d'Hulst, however, unhesitatingly published the picture as an early work of Jacob Jordaens (1982). On examining the picture closely, the attribution to Jordaens seems entirely convincing. It has been accepted

Fig. 1: Heindrick van Balen, *Naiads Filling the Horn of Plenty.* Mauritshuis, The Hague.

by Christopher Brown (verbal information, 1986), and Held and Haverkamp Begemann agree. Jordaens, of course, fits the description of "an artist very much under Rubens' influence". At least when the picture was painted, c. 1615, Rubens's influence on the young artist was still very strong. Hence it is not surprising that the nymphs and putti in the Bass composition have the rosy flesh tones, golden hair, and earthy plumpness of Rubens's nudes.

The seated nymph in the right foreground, holding the horn of plenty, closely resembles Rubens's *Venus Frigida*, painted c. 1612-1615, in Kassel (catalogue no. 85). The subject in its entirety, however, and its compositional scheme comprising a circle of intertwined bodies, partly seated or standing on the ground, partly climbing up and suspended from the trees, was derived from one of the graceful, lighthearted mythological scenes by Hendrick van Balen, who was a teacher of Anthony van Dyck. Van Balen's influence on Jordaens's early work has been acknowledged by d'Hulst (p. 48). The composition of the Bass painting is clearly inspired by Van Balen's *Naiads Filling the Horn of Plenty* in the Mauritshuis (fig. 1), but for his figures Jordaens preferred the vigorous Rubenesque type to the elegant daintiness of Van Balen's. The Bass painting demonstrates how the young artist synthesized the stimuli received in Antwerp from both the powerful presence of Rubens and the more subtle poetic manner of the attractive 'little master,' Van Balen.

Jordaens's composition is more dynamic than Van Balen's. He shifted the seated figure of Fertility, holding the horn of plenty, from her central position to the right, thus adding tension to Van Balen's perfectly balanced circular arrangement. Van Balen's female satyr on the left is moved towards the center, to make room for the addition of three putti carrying a basket of fruit, and a goat. Jordaens further added a satyr on the far right, driving away a tiger and a lion, who might endanger the idyllic scene. Van Balen's ballet-like harmony is here transformed into a dynamic scene full of energetic movement and tension. Jordaens's vigorous temperament is beginning to assert itself. Another of his early mythological scenes, the *Bacchanal* from the Nardus Collection, Paris (d'Hulst, fig. 21, p. 54), is inspired more exclusively by Rubens. The theme of the Bass painting is repeated in the *Allegory of Fruitfulness* (c. 1617) in Munich (d'Hulst, fig. 44, pp. 75, 77), a huge and imposing painting that shows the artist's fully developed characteristic style. By comparison, the Bass painting appears like a preliminary study. Allegories of fruitfulness or abundance were popular in Flanders at a time when the Twelve Years Truce between Spain and the Northern Netherlands (1609-1621) raised hopes of a new Golden Age of peace and plenty. Jordaens executed several other versions of this theme.

M.A.R.

Condition: Fair condition.

MARCELLUS KOFFERMANS

Flemish, active 1549-1579

Marcellus Koffermans was an Antwerp painter who was admitted as a master to the St. Lucas Guild in 1549. His name appears in the records of the guild on various other occasions, but details of his life are not known. Although a contemporary of Pieter Bruegel the Elder, Koffermans painted in an archaicizing style, variously following the manner of Schöngauer, Memling, Gerard David, and other masters of an earlier generation. His paintings are usually on a small scale; dated works are from the years 1561 to 1570.

The Holy Family with an Angel (63.19 {a})

Panel, *118.5 x 92.9 (46¼ x 36¼)*.

At an unknown time before 1924, two wing panels were attached to this painting to form a triptych. The wing panels did not originally belong to the composition. See Flemish School, sixteenth century, 63.19 [b].

Provenance

Galerie Fischer, Luzern, 8 September 1924, No. 145.
Oberstdivisionär Pfyffer v. Altishofen (as recorded by Fischer, see below).
Galerie Fischer, Luzern, 16-20 November 1954, No. 1846.
Baron de Grundherr, Castle Mittersill, Austria.
Parke-Bernet, 24 October 1962, No. 39.
Bass Collection, 1963.

References

Frau A. Pestalozzi-Pfyffer, *Meister ES und die Schöngauer* (as major work by Martin Schöngauer).
W. R. Valentiner, Certificate, Raleigh NC, 14 March 1956 (Koffermans).
Max J. Friedlander, Certificate, Amsterdam, 24 September 1956 (Koffermans).
Bass Catalogue 1973, No. 19.

The panel depicts the Virgin enthroned in a landscape, with the nude child in her lap. An angel on the right is offering a bunch of grapes, symbol of the eucharist, to the Christ Child. A dignified elderly male figure, dressed in clerical robes, occupies an ambiguous space close to the Virgin, but on a different level and half hidden by her mantle. This figure has been traditionally interpreted as St. Joseph, justifying the picture's title of *Holy Family.* But, unlike the Virgin, the Child and the angel, his features are not generalized but have a portrait-like character.

Koffermans derived his composition from an earlier work, an altarpiece painted c. 1510 by the Master of St. Sang, now called *The Holy Family* but previously known as *Madonna and Child with Donor and an Angel* (Kunsthalle Hamburg; fig. 1). The male figure in this painting closely resembles the 'Joseph' in the Bass picture. The Master of St. Sang was a member of the confraternity of the Holy Blood at Bruges, and the male figure, dressed

as a cleric, could have been a donor belonging to the same order. However, a donor was conventionally depicted in profile, turned in adoration towards the holy personages, while the Master of St. Sang's figure looks straight at the beholder, without any reference to the Virgin and Child. The pose of the male figure in the Hamburg panel is in fact consistent with the tradition of an artist's self-portrait. From Renaissance times onwards artists frequently painted their own portrait into religious (and later secular) groups. The artist's face in such paintings is identifiable by being fully turned towards the beholder. The close proximity of this figure to the Virgin and Child is, however, unprecedented for either a donor's portrait or a self-portrait.

The Master of St. Sang may have intended to pose in the role of St. Joseph, thus introducing a new iconography, since the pose and character of the male figure are unprecedented in previous depictions of the saint. This work seems to have inspired a new type of *Holy Family* in

Fig. 1: Master of St. Sang, *The Holy Family* (Triptych), c. 1510-1520, Hamburg, Kunsthalle (No. 196).

paintings by contemporary Flemish artists. By the time Koffermans painted his version, four to five decades later, the Master of St. Sang's male portrait had become fully accepted as a figure representing St. Joseph in a Holy Family group.

Koffermans' painting retains the Master of St. Sang's figure group with hardly any alteration, but the artist substitutes a landscape view for the interior space in the Hamburg painting, to allow for the changing taste in Flemish painting since the earlier part of the century.

The Koffermans composition was repeated in many copies and variations, which seem to have been in demand both in Flanders and in Spain, where the artist's work is well represented. The popularity of the composition suggests that in Koffermans's time the Master of St. Sang's donor painting had become the prototype of a new concept of Joseph and the Holy Family. The type of Joseph reading a book and holding or wearing glasses is an iconographic novelty that occurred mainly in the Netherlands in the early part of the sixteenth century. Up to the end of the fifteenth century, St. Joseph was usually represented as a dignified elderly biblical figure, or as a humble carpenter. The changing role of St. Joseph, from a simple artisan performing manual tasks to the scholarly thinker or humanist portrayed in the Bass picture, can be linked with contemporary developments in the teachings of the

Catholic Church. Similar images of the saint with book and glasses occur in works by the Master of the Death of the Virgin (National Gallery, London, No. 2603) and by Joos van Cleve, and in other paintings by the Master of St. Sang. The startling change in the iconography of St. Joseph as represented in the Bass painting has received little or no scholarly attention so far, but is now the subject of a much needed study.[1]

Koffermans and his studio painted many versions of this composition.[2] One of these until recently belonged to the San Diego Museum of Art (Catalogue 1947, p. 109). It was sold at Sotheby's, New York, 15 January 1987, lot 1. This painting is clearly a smaller copy after the Bass picture, and it is in poor condition. A seventeenth-century copy belongs to the University of California at Los Angeles. Another copy was exhibited in the 1929-1930 exhibition at Seville, Spain. This version had portraits in medallions on either side (see San Diego Museum Catalogue 1947).

M.A.R.

1. Bernadine Heller-Greenman, *The Iconography of St. Joseph in the Holy Family Painting by Marcellus Koffermans, Bass Museum of Art, Miami Beach, and Related Works.* Master's Thesis for the University of Miami, in preparation.
2. Heller-Greenman, ibid, lists fourteen.

Condition: The support consists of four vertical panels which, although very thin, are in perfect condition. The paint is of very high quality (no cracks have developed) which speaks for the excellent technique of the artist.

THOMAS LAWRENCE, P.R.A.

English, 1769-1830

A boy-prodigy, Thomas Lawrence made his name first as a taker of pencil profiles at his father's inn at Devizes, and then as a pastellist at Bath. He settled in London in 1787 and began to paint in oils. His success was immediate and continuing and culminated in his official mission to Europe, 1818-1819, to paint the allied military leaders and heads of state who were responsible for the defeat of Napoleon. These portraits, now in the Waterloo Chamber at Windsor Castle, are his monument, and the portrait of Pope Pius VII is his masterpiece.

Sir Charles Cockerell, 1st Baronet, and His Family (63.34)

Probably painted c. 1817.

Canvas, *241 x 169.2 (94 x 66).*

Provenance

Christie's, London, Sir Charles Rushout, 4th Bt., Sale, 2 July 1920, lot 41.

Christie's, London, Lord Essendon Sale, 18 June 1954, lot 60.

Christie's, London, The Late R. W. Lloyd Sale, 29 May 1959, lot 84.

Bass Collection

References

K. Garlick, *A Catalogue of the Paintings, Drawings and Pastels of Sir Thomas Lawrence,* Walpole Society, vol. XXXIX, London, 1964, p. 56.

Bass Catalogue 1973, No. 34.

K. Garlick, *Sir Thomas Lawrence,* Oxford 1989, p. 170.

Sir Charles Cockerell, M.P., a British civil servant in Bengal, was in India, 1774-1800, and was created a baronet in 1809 for his services. In 1789 he had married a daughter of Sir Charles William Blunt, 2nd Bt., but she died in the same year. In 1808 he married, secondly, the Hon. Harriet Rushout, a daughter of the 1st Lord Northwick, who is shown here with him and their three children, Charles (1809-1869), who assumed his mother's name of Rushout and on the death of his father in 1837 confusingly became Sir Charles Rushout, 2nd Bt. (not Sir Charles Cockerell, 2nd Bt.), Harriet Anne, who became Viscountess Deerhurst and died in 1842, and Maria Elizabeth, who died in 1832.

Sir Charles was the younger brother of the architect Samuel Pepys Cockerell who, c. 1805, built for him Sezincote House, near Moreton-in-Marsh, Gloucestershire, an extraordinary mansion in the moorish style which still survives as a private house. Their paternal grandmother was a great-niece of Samuel Pepys, the diarist, and was residuary legatee to the Pepys estate.

This fine portrait group was not exhibited in Lawrence's lifetime, was not engraved, and was virtually unknown until it appeared in the London saleroom of Christie's in 1920. Nor is there any reference to it in contemporary literature. It is, for this reason, difficult to date, as Lawrence's style in middle life varied little over the years. Assuming that the boy is under ten years of age, the group must have been painted c. 1817-1818, before Lawrence set out on his continental mission in September of the latter year. This seems to be the most likely date. If, however, the boy is assumed to be over ten years of age, the date cannot be before March 1820, when Lawrence returned to England. A child in a pose similar to that of the small girl crouched on the steps appears in *The Best Children* by Lawrence now in the collection of Dr. Armand Hammer.

K.J.G.

Condition: Cleaned and relined in 1988. Excellent condition.

JEAN-BAPTISTE VAN LOO, Attributed to

French, 1684-1745

Born at Aix-en-Provence, the first son of Louis Abraham van Loo, Jean-Baptiste, belonged to a dynasty of painters of Dutch origin who settled in the south of France in the late seventeenth century. Trained by his father, Jean-Baptiste specialized in history painting, genre, and portraiture. Among his patrons were the Prince of Savoy and the Duke of Carignan. After travels to Monaco, Turin, and Rome, he went to Paris, was patronized by Louis XV, and became a professor of the academy. Financial misfortunes forced him to return to Aix in 1735. With the exception of four years spent in London, 1738-1742, he remained in Aix where he was active almost exclusively as a portrait painter.

Portrait of a Lady as Goddess Pomona (79.132)

Canvas, *146.1 x 112.8 (57 x 44).*

Provenance
Collection Dd. Perrier, Geneva.
Galerie Fischer, Luzern.
Purchased 28 August 1965 for the Bass Collection.

References
Reports by G. Fiocco, H. Zimmerman, Ludwig Baldass, Zürich 1955 (all certifying an attribution to Jean-Marc Nattier).
Herman Vos, Report, Munich 1957 (tentative attribution to Carlo [Charles André] van Loo).
José Pijoan, *Summa Artis,* vol. XVI, Madrid 1957, p. 294, fig. 425 (as Nattier).
Bass Catalogue 1973, No. 132 (as Nattier).

The painting shows a lady dressed in a rich peach-colored gown with low-cut bodice. In her left hand she holds a flower, and in her right a pruning staff. A putto holds up to her a basket of fruit, and more fruit is scattered on the ground. A tall tree and a classical urn on a pedestal on her right set off the landscape background. Her accessories indicate that the sitter is posing in the role of Pomona, a Roman goddess who is the protectress of gardens, orchards, and fruit. Her attribute is a basket of fruit or a cornucopia. She is generally seated under a tree and holds a pruning knife.

Pomona is traditionally depicted with her suitor Vertumnus as he approaches her in the disguise of an old woman (Ovid, *Metamorphoses,* 14:623-697 and 765-771). The goddess of gardens is an unusual character to be used in portraiture. Aristocratic French ladies preferred to pose as more ethereal mythological figures, such as Flora, Diana, or Hebe. However, Louis XIV through his grand scheme of the gardens of Versailles and his own fascination with horticulture had made gardening a fashionable pastime. Hence society ladies did not hesitate to have themselves portrayed *en jardinière,* dressed as a lady gardener.

The Bass picture closely resembles van Loo's portrait of *Mme. d'Albert en Jardinière,* signed and dated 1736, in the Musée Granet, Aix-en-Provence. The sitter is posed with a basket of fruit and a pruning knife. She is dressed in the 'simple' costume of a lady gardener, without any jewelry. Mme. d'Albert's portrait omits the putto and the landscape, but her type is very similar to the sitter of the Bass portrait, who chose a mythological interpretation of the gardening theme. Both ladies have a matronly fullness of figure and an amiable, warm expression. They seem to belong to a provincial upper class milieu or the minor aristocracy, rather than to court society. The more elaborate setting of the Bass portrait suggests perhaps a higher social status than Mme. d'Albert's. The treatment of the face (with the suggestion of a double-chin), of the pudgy hands and arms, and of the satin drapery, is extremely close in both portraits.

At least three prominent members of the Van Loo family painted portraits of lady gardeners, but Charles Amedée van Loo's portrait of *Mme. Pompadour,* [1] and Louis Michel van Loo's *Portrait of a Lady,* signed and dated 1760, [2] are more studiedly graceful and are painted with the delicate brushwork and light palette of the fully developed rococo style. The matronly type of the Bass lady and Mme. d'Albert portraits, together with their firmly controlled brushwork and saturated colors, hark back to the late baroque phase of French painting as exemplified by Largillière and Rigaud. The Bass picture, which has been wrongly attributed to Nattier, could be close in date to the Musée Granet portrait, that is c. 1736.

M.A.R.

1. M. Knoedler and Co., New York, Nov. 23 - Dec. 11, 1943, Cat. p. 12 (10).
2. Countess Sale Collection, New York. Published in *International Studio,* 86, April 1927, pp. 21-28.

Condition: Very good condition.

MASTER OF THE REVALER ST. ELIZABETH LEGEND

German (Lübeck), active c. 1480-1500

The artist, whose name is unknown, was a collaborator of the prominent Lübeck master Bernt Notke (1440-1509). He is called by the name of his best-known work, the four scenes of the Legend of St. Elizabeth on the 'Sunday-side' of Notke's altarpiece in the Geistkirche (Church of the Holy Spirit) in Reval, near Lübeck. As one of Notke's most able assistants, the Master of the Revaler St. Elizabeth Legend executed several other paintings, for instance the Thuro altarpiece in the Copenhagen National Museum. In spite of a somewhat dry and stiff provincial manner, this artist's work is competently painted and has a certain naive charm, with a flair for narrative and genre, as demonstrated in the Reval altarpiece.[1]

Four wings of a Passion Altar (63.20)

Painted c. 1499.

Tempera on four panels,
inner wings each 165 x 49 (65 x 19.3),
outer wings each 165 x 44 (65 x 17.3).

Provenance
Collection Baron Swansea, Builth Wells (Wales).

References
Alfred Stange, Certificate, 29 December 1956.
Alfred Stange, *Kritisches Verzeichnis der deutschen Tafelbilder vor Dürer,* vol. 1, Munich 1967, p. 210, no. 685.
Bass Catalogue 1973, No. 20.

Exhibitions
Geneva, Galerie Fischer and Mme. Adine Genrouix, *Exposition de Tableaux Anciens des Grands Maîtres,* 1957, no. 18.

Altarpieces with scenes of the Passion *(Passionsaltar)* were a specialty of Northern European art in the late Middle Ages and early Renaissance. They usually consisted of a number of hinged panels, painted on both sides, with the outer panels normally kept closed to cover the inside of the inner panels. The insides were displayed only on Sundays or during religious festivals (Sonntagsseite or Feiertagsseite). Sometimes the display side consisted of carvings rather than paintings, as in the case of the Bass altarpiece, where the carved reliefs on the reverse of the inner panels are lost.

The two inner wings (C, D) and the insides of the outer wings (A, B) are painted with eight scenes of the Passion; on the upper tier: Ecce Homo, Carrying of the Cross, Nailing to the Cross, Crucifixion; and on the lower tier: Lamentation, Entombment, Christ in Limbo, and the Risen Christ. On the outsides (verso) of the outer wings are four scenes of preceding events: The Last Supper, Capture of Christ, Christ before Herod, and the Flagellation.

The painter based his individual scenes on prints by well known contemporary artists. For instance, the Ecce Homo is derived from Martin Schöngauer's engraving (B.15), and the Last Supper from the Master of Zwolle. The Master of the Revaler St. Elizabeth Altar did not slavishly copy these scenes but freely adapted them according to his own ideas. According to Stange, the wings date from c. 1499 and are thus a mature work of the master (ref. Stange 1956).

M.A.R.

1. See Alfred Stange, *Deutsche Malerei der Gothik,* Munich/Berlin 1954, p. 114f.

Condition: Good condition. Some portions of the sky have been regilded, but much of the gold paint is the original. The frames have been clumsily repainted and haphazardly re-engaged with new hinges, probably in the 19th or early 20th century.

A   C   Front view   D   B

nner wings   B   Outer wing   Verso of B

Verso of A   A   Outer wing   C and D

MICHIEL VAN MUSSCHER

Dutch, 1645-1705

Michiel van Musscher was born in Rotterdam and his first recorded teacher (1660) was Martin Saagmolen. In 1661, he was in Amsterdam as the pupil of the history and portrait painter Abraham van den Tempel. Four years later he was studying with Gabriel Metsu, the famous Amsterdam painter of genre scenes and portraits, and in 1667 he spent three months working with Adriaen van Ostade in Haarlem. By the following year he had returned to his native city of Rotterdam, but eventually settled in Amsterdam where he married Eva Visscher in 1678, and became a citizen ten years later. After his first wife's death he married Elsie Klanes in 1693.

Van Musscher's early work includes genre scenes, influenced by the Leyden School, but later he became fashionable as a painter of portraits 'in the French manner.' A Swedish architect, describing his visit to Amsterdam in 1687, found that the best portrait painters were David van der Plaas "on a large scale," and Nicholas Maes and Michiel van Musscher "on a small scale."[1] Van Musscher made a specialty of painting artists in their studios, and a number of such scenes are self-portraits.

Self Portrait of the Artist in His Studio (63.2)*

An inscription on the little box to the right of the artist was once read as *VM*, but is no longer readable.

Canvas, *59 x 49.5 (23 x 19¼).*

Provenance
Collection Baron Floriet, Paris.
Dealer M. Brandt, New York, 1957/58.
W. Hillsborough, London, 1959.
W. Suhr, New York, 1960, sold to Bass Collection.

References
C. J. Holmes, "Two Youthful Experiments by Vermeer of Delft (?)," *Burlington Magazine,* 15, 1909, pp. 246-47, with reproduction.
Christopher Wright, *Vermeer,* London 1976, p. 74 with reproduction (as Vermeer).
D. Hannema, "Problemen rondom Vermeer van Delft," *Boymans Bijdragen,* 1978, p. 89f. with reproduction (as Vermeer).
S. Rees Jones (Courtauld Institute, London), Letter to John Bass, date unknown (the letter is recorded in the Bass Catalogue but it can no longer be traced).
Bass Catalogue 1973, no. 2. (Vermeer, attr.).
Margarita Russell, "The Artist in His Studio: A Self-portrait by Michiel van Musscher," *Apollo,* January 1988, p. 9f.

The picture shows a young painter seated behind a table, surrounded by objects belonging to his studio and gazing at the beholder with captivating directness. It has been widely known in the earlier part of this century as a self-portrait by Johannes Vermeer. Most of the older literature on Vermeer associated the portrait with the picture listed in the catalogue of the auction of Vermeer's paintings in Amsterdam, 16 May, 1696: "No. 3 Portrait of Vermeer in a room with various accessories, uncommonly well painted by himself, Fl. 45.-."

The attribution to Vermeer was based on two supposed pieces of evidence: (a) the letters inscribed on the box shown in the lower left corner of the still-life displayed on the artist's easel, which are no longer decipherable but once were read as Vermeer's initials; and (b) the existence of an engraving which reproduces the scene of the Bass picture in reverse and is inscribed in ink by a later hand on the lower margin with the names of Vermeer as the painter and Joannes Meyssens (1612-1670) as the engraver and publisher (fig. 1). The print is known only from a photograph by Giraudon (G.27.351), taken in 1927 when Giraudon also photographed the painting then in the collection of Baron Floriet, Paris. The print has been widely published as being in the Bibliothèque Nationale, but this is not the case. Its present whereabouts are unknown.

As late as 1978, D. Hannema published the engraving with the remark that it was done c. 1650 after the portrait of Vermeer (ref. Hannema). However Albert Blankert, whose scholarly manuscript on Vermeer was first published in 1975, did not include the Bass painting in his oeuvre catalogue.[2]

Since the publication of Blankert's monograph, the attribution to Vermeer has lost any credibility. The rejection of Vermeer's authorship on stylistic grounds can be supported by the dating of the young man's costume: the kimono-style gown and cravat he is wearing (referred to as an 'Indian Gown' in the seventeenth century) first made their appearance in the 1660s. In fact, the costume expert of the Victoria & Albert Museum (Avril Hart) dated the Bass picture to c. 1665-1669. At that time Vermeer, born 1632, would have been in his thirties, but the sitter of the Bass painting can be little older than twenty; hence the date previously given to the painting was c. 1651, when Vermeer was nineteen years old (ref. Bass Cat. 1973). A date around 1650 is suggested in most of the earlier literature.

The Bass Museum changed its attribution from 'Vermeer (attr.)' to 'Circle of Vermeer,' and scholars familiar with the painting offered various suggestions as to the identity of the artist: Samuel van Hoogstraeten, Cornelis de Man, Johannes Voorhout, Wallerand Vaillant are among the names proffered.[3]

However, none of these artists' works comes as close to the Bass painting as a self-portrait by Michiel van Musscher, signed and dated 1679, in the Historisch Museum, Rotterdam (fig. 2). Van Musscher's portrait bears an outstanding resemblance to the young artist in the Bass painting, allowing for the fact that the sitter has aged about fifteen years. The artists in both portraits wear identical gowns and caps. The objects in the studio are displayed in a similar manner on a table top which occupies the first plane. A Smyrna rug covers the table and a curtain partly frames the space in both compositions. The figure of the putto blowing bubbles in the Bass portrait is also present in the later painting, though in a different pose, and the lute has been moved from the wall into the foreground. Open books are displayed in a very similar fashion. Most importantly, the space concept, with the artist and his possessions viewed at a 45° angle from above, and the distribution of light are analogous. Besides, there exists an intangible affinity between the two compositions which cannot be 'scientifically' explained but which speaks directly to the beholder's sensibility. A third self-portrait by Van Musscher, dated 1690, shows the artist still in the same gown and cap, with his features further aged to reflect the lapse of years since the 1679 portrait.[4] The Bass painting, which must date from the mid 1660s, seems to be the earliest of a cycle showing the painter in his studio at various phases of his life.

Close in style to the Bass painting is another early work, the *Portrait of an Artist in his Studio,* in the collection of Lord Northbrook.[5] The date on this signed painting has been read 165__, but van Musscher was only 15 in 1660 and it seems unlikely that he could have achieved such an accomplished composition at such an early age. The painting, like the Bass portrait, must date from the mid 1660s. The distribution of light, the fleeting shadows cast by objects hanging or leaning against a wall, the *pentimenti* around the sitter's sleeves and head are done almost identically in both paintings. Both suggest the influence of Gabriel Metsu, with whom Van Musscher studied in 1665, when he was twenty years of age.

The fact that van Musscher's initials repeat the V and M of Vermeer's once read in the Bass painting adds conviction to the re-attribution of this picture to an artist whose interest in self-portraiture seems to have started at an early age. Michiel van Musscher's manner hardened in his later work,[6] but for his self-portraits in the studio (1679 and 1690) he maintained a felicitous lightness of touch and a certain easy-going charm that has endeared the artist to the public.

M.A.R.

*I am indebted to Egbert Haverkamp Begemann for making many helpful suggestions and encouraging the line of research that led to an assured attribution to Van Musscher. Professor Begemann fully accepts this attribution.

1. Dr. Gustav Upmark, "Ein Besuch in Holland 1687: aus den Reiseschilderungen des schwedischen Architekten Nicodemus Tessin," *Oud Holland,* 18, 1900, p. 126.
2. According to a note in the files of the RKD, The Hague, Blankert saw the Bass painting in 1969 and considered it the work of a weak artist (meaning, presumably, by comparison with Vermeer).
3. In the RKD, the Bass painting is currently filed under Job Berckheyde, presumably with reference to the painter's studio scene, dated 1659, in the Hermitage, Leningrad.
4. The portrait in a Swiss private collection is reproduced in *Apollo,* January 1988, p. 12, fig. 3 (see ref. Russell).
5. Ibid. p. 13, fig. 4. This work is widely known as a portrait of the marine painter Willem van de Velde the Younger, but the identification of the sitter is controversial.
6. The portrait of *Michiel II Comans and his Wife* (Rijksmuseum, Amsterdam) painted in 1669 is already rendered in a darker and more firmly controlled manner. The so-called self-portrait in the Pushkin Museum, Moscow, done in a similar manner and also dated 1669, shows an artist significantly older than the twenty-four-year-old Van Musscher; it must be the portrait of another artist.

Condition: The picture was re-lined and cleaned in 1960. In the re-lining process the paint layer was flattened and has taken on the pattern of the canvas weave. Many areas are abraded and major passages thin and transparent. The picture is covered with discolored varnish. Minute age craquelure throughout.

Fig. 1: Johannes Meyssens (?). *An Artist in His Studio*.
Engraving after M. van Musscher's self-portrait in the Bass Collection.
Inscribed on the lower margin by a later hand:
Ver Meer pinxit and *Joannes Meysens fecit et excud.*
Photo Giraudon G.27.351.

Fig. 2: Michiel van Musscher. *Self-portrait*.
Signed and dated: *M:v:Musscher./pinxit./A: 1679*.
Historisch Museum der Stad Rotterdam.

WILLIAM OWEN, A.R.A.

British, 1769-1825

Painter of portraits and scenes of rustic life, William Owen was a native of Ludlow in Shropshire but settled in London in 1786 where he had considerable success and was appointed Principal Painter to the Prince of Wales in 1810, following the death of Hoppner. He had a strong individual style which is often characterized by an emphasis on the bone structure of the faces of his sitters. He painted little after 1820.

Sophia Hutchins Callcott (79.257)

Painted c. 1815-1820.

Inscription on back of canvas: *Sophy Hutchins Callcott by Owen daughter of Dr. Calcott 1815-20.*

Canvas, *63.5 x 78.8 (30¾ x 25).*

Label on back inscribed: *McClees Galleries. Est. 1845. 1807 Walnut St., Philadelphia.*

Provenance
Christie's Sale, 6 March 1914 (anonymous seller).
McClees Galleries, Philadelphia.
Parke-Bernet Galleries, New York, 3 November 1967, lot 80.

References
Bass Catalogue 1973, No. 257.

Sophia Hutchins Callcott, born 1794, was a daughter of John Wall Callcott (1766-1821) and his wife, Elizabeth Mary Hutchins (1775-1825). Her father was a composer. He was a lecturer in music at the Royal Institution, London, 1806, and in that year published a *Musical Grammar.* Her uncle was the landscape artist Sir Augustus Wall Callcott, R.A., a friend and rival of J.M.W. Turner, whose work was celebrated by an exhibition at the Tate Gallery as recently as 1981. William Owen was one of Callcott's closest friends and his portrait of Callcott, seated in Van Dyck dress, is now in H.M. British Embassy, Santiago.

K.J.G.

Condition: The painting is in good condition.

HYACINTHE RIGAUD

French, 1649-1743

Hyacinthe Rigaud was the prominent court painter during the last phase of the reign of Louis XIV. He retained his popularity during the regency and under Louis XV. Rigaud combined elegant poses and dazzling costume and settings with a sensitive understanding of the sitter's character. His most famous work is the majestic portrait of Louis XIV, painted in 1701, now in the Louvre. In his more personal work such as the portrait of his mother now in the Louvre, Rigaud was influenced by Rembrandt.

Hans William Bentinck, Earl of Portland, K.G. (1649-1709) (63.31)

Painted 1698-1699

Inscribed on lower right: *WILLIAM BENTINCK EARL OF PORTLAND.*

Canvas, *135.9 x 107.7 (53 x 42)*. Circa *3.8 cm.* all round are covered by the frame—unframed *137 x 110 (54 x 43¼)*. An extra *2.5cm.* on left and right seem to be pulled round the stretcher.

Labels on reverse:
1891 Billard Room No. 29
Jan. 29 THE HON. HENRY ROBERT BRAND
½ L. Port. of William Bentinck
Earl of Portland
(unframed)
on Wt of fireplace
1891 Hon. H.R. Manes
Jan. 28 Line out to 54½ x 43½'
[Restorer's label?]

Gilded and carved Kentian style frame of great distinction.

Provenance
(?) The Hon. Henry Robert Brand, 1891.
Viscount Hampden, at The Hoo, 1910.
Christie's, London, Sale 29 May 1959, No. 96.

References
J. Roman, *Le Livre de raison du peintre Hyacinthe Rigaud,* Paris 1919, p. 64.
Richard W. Goulding and C.K. Adams, *Catalogue of the Pictures Belonging to His Grace the Duke of Portland, K.G.,* Cambridge 1936, pp. 58-59, no. 148.
National Portrait Gallery, London, *British Historical Portraits: A Selection from the National Portrait Gallery with Biographical Notes,* Cambridge 1957, p. 178.
David Piper, *Catalogue of Seventeenth-Century Portraits in the National Portrait Gallery 1625-1714,* Cambridge 1963, p. 283, no. 1968.
Bass Catalogue 1973, no. 31.

Hans William Bentinck was the son of a Dutch nobleman, Baron Bentinck of Diepenheim. He entered the service of William of Orange at an early age and became his close and devoted friend. When William succeeded to the English throne in 1688, Bentinck accompanied him to England and stayed with him. He continued to enjoy the King's confidence and received the title Earl of Portland in recognition of his services. Bentinck served in the Battle of the Boyne, and in 1697 negotiated the terms of the Treaty of Ryswick.

In 1698, Bentinck, now called Lord Portland, was in Paris as the King's Ambassador Extraordinary, conducting delicate negotiations regarding the Spanish succession and Anglo-French relations. He was a successful diplomat and on very friendly terms with Louis XIV. During his mission in Paris he sat to Rigaud for his portrait.

The painting shows the Earl in three-quarter-length figure, standing on the left, his right hand on the baton extended to the right. He wears a voluminous powdered wig and black armor, with a wide red sash tied in a large bow on his right. Draped over his left shoulder is the blue ribbon of the Order of the Garter with the 'George' suspended from it.

The original portrait is believed to be that in the Duke of Portland's collection at Welbeck Abbey (ref. Goulding), but according to contemporary correspondence between the Earl and Mathew Prior, and to other sources, Rigaud

WILLIAM BENTINCK
EARL OF PORTLAND

painted at least two replicas with his own hand (ref. Goulding, p. 59). Indeed Rigaud himself recorded two of his copies in *Le Livre de raison*. Goulding lists seven replicas (which he calls 'repetitions'), two of which were made in the twentieth century. The Bass painting ('repetition' No. 3) is described by Goulding as "probably an old copy."

The painting resembles most closely the version in the National Portrait Gallery, London, No. 1968 (Goulding 'repetition' 5). This version is inscribed *William Bentinck/ Earl of Portland, 1697*. The National Portrait Gallery lists it as a studio copy. Both paintings are about 5 inches wider than the Duke of Portland's version, and the added width is an extension of the landscape, mostly on the left. In the National Portrait Gallery painting, however, the wide red sash, which appears on all the other versions, is omitted.

The sash was worn by officers as a sign of rank, and Bentinck was a General of the English Horse and also commander of a regiment of Dutch Guards. He was made a Knight of the Garter (K.G.) in 1697.

The quality of the Bass Museum portrait is superior to the version in the National Portrait Gallery, London. The Bass picture is most likely one of the two replicas executed largely by Rigaud himself. The landscape, like that in the Duke of Portland's version, was painted by J. Perrocel, Rigaud's foremost collaborator on landscape backgrounds (ref. *Livre de Raison,* p.64). The striking pose of the sitter was very popular with Rigaud's aristocratic patrons and was used for portraits of King Louis XIV and other royal personages.

M.A.R.

Condition: Good condition.

GEORGE ROMNEY

British, 1734-1802

Born comparatively humbly and trained by an itinerant portraitist, George Romney came to London from the north of England in 1762 and very soon established himself as a fashionable painter whose style exhibited an appealing spontaneity. He won a reputation for his many studies and finished portraits of Emma, Lady Hamilton. His weakness was over-facility. There was, however, an intellectual side to his nature which remained unfulfilled. He was in many ways an outsider, never becoming a member of the Royal Academy, and he suffered a mental collapse in the last decade of his life. In 1798, Romney left London for good and retired to his family in his native county of Cumberland. He had lived for thirty-six years in London but his wife and children had never joined him. In recent years the Museum and Art Gallery at Kendal, Abbott Hall, has become a small center of Romney studies and some excellent examples of his painting may be seen there.

Mrs. Thomson Bonar and Her Daughter (63.35)

Painted 1790-1794.

Canvas, *150 x 117.9 (58½ x 46).*

Provenance
Christie's, London, Thomson Bonar Sale, 9 May 1896, Lot 119; purchased by Agnew's, London.
Knoedler Gallery, New York.
Frederick A. Szarvasy, 1950.
W. R. Lloyd, Christie's Sale, 29 May 1959, lot 98.

References
Humphry Ward and W. Roberts, *Romney,* London 1904, vol. I, p. 14.
Bass Catalogue 1973, No. 35.

Anne, daughter of Andrew Thomson, married her cousin, Thomson Bonar, a merchant who had trading connections with Russia. Their daughter, Agnes, who according to Ward and Roberts (see ref.), was an only child, married a Count Moretti. It is very possible that Mrs. Bonar was a second wife as it seems that Thomson Bonar had a son who succeeded to his property in 1813. The Bonars lived at Camden Place, Chislehurst, and were a much liked and respected couple. It was a sensation on almost a national scale when in August 1813 they were murdered in their beds by their Irish butler. Mr. Bonar was then seventy. The age of Mrs. Bonar is not recorded. The murder was

unpremeditated and without apparent motive. A graphic account is given in *The Gentleman's Magazine,* (1813, vol. I, p. 583). On page 656 of the same volume there is a description of the hanging of the butler, Philip Nicholson, "amidst an immense throng of spectators."

Sittings for the portrait are recorded in Romney's sitter-books between December 1790 and January 1794. Payment of £ 104 was received in December 1794.

It is clear that Romney had a sympathy and a special gift for mother-and-child portraits, painting a number of them. He was in Italy from 1773 to 1775, where the Madonna-and-Child compositions of Raphael strongly appealed to him. A fine exercise in this manner is *Mrs. Johnstone and Son* in the Tate Gallery. The Bonar group, painted late in his career, is less successful in composition but retains an Italian tenderness.

Condition: The paint is very cracked but secure.

ROMNEY

Mrs. John Charnock (79.320)

Canvas, *125.6 x 100 (49 x 39).*

Provenance
Arthur Sanderson, Edinburgh, 1904.
Christie's, London, Arthur Sanderson Sale, 3 July 1908,
lot 85; bought by the dealer Fischoff, Paris.
Sedelmeyer, Paris.
T.J. Blakeslee, New York.
T.B. Walker, Minneapolis (purchased from
Blakeslee, 1912).
Parke-Bernet, Sale of Old Master and English paintings
from the Walker Art Center, Minneapolis, 21 April 1971,
lot 187.
Bass Museum, 1971.

References
Ward and Roberts, *Romney,* vol. II, p. 28.
Bass Catalogue 1973, No. 320.

Exhibitions
St. Paul, Minnesota, St. Paul Institution, April 1920.

Romney's sitter-books record nine sittings for Mrs.
Charnock in August and September 1795, a period which
marked the beginning of the decline of his powers. Little
seems to be known about this lady or her husband. It
appears that their home was Rossie Castle, Tayside,
Scotland, as it was here, according to *The Gentleman's
Magazine,* that a daughter was born to them in 1800, and
it was at Rossie Castle in 1807 that Mrs. Charnock
married her second husband, Thomas Hamilton.

K.J.G.

Condition: Fair Condition.

PETER PAUL RUBENS and Studio

Flemish, 1577-1640

Peter Paul Rubens was born in Siegen, Westphalia, where his family lived in exile. Returning with them to Antwerp after his father's death in 1587, he trained with Tobias Verhaecht, Adam van Noort, and ultimately Otto van Veen who had the greatest influence on his development. In 1598 he became a Master of the Antwerp Guild of St. Luke, and in 1600 he went to Italy where he became court painter to the Duke of Mantua. Remaining in Italy for eight years, he received important commissions in Mantua, Genoa, and Rome. In 1608, he returned to Antwerp where he married Isabella Brant, daughter of a magistrate.

Rubens served as court painter to the Archdukes Albert and Isabella. With the help of a huge well-organized studio, he executed spectacular commissions for the royal courts of Europe, among them the cycle of the life of the French Queen Marie de Medici (now in the Louvre), the ceiling of the Banqueting Hall at Whitehall for King Charles I (who gave him a knighthood), and numerous paintings for King Philip IV of Spain. He filled the churches of Flanders with large altarpieces and at the same time painted many portraits. Rubens is considered the founder of the baroque style in European painting. His art owes a great deal to Titian, for whom he had a lasting admiration. A scholar and diplomat as well as an artist, he was the friend of kings and noblemen and was himself called the 'prince of painters' in acknowledgement of his outstanding artistic achievement and the elevated social status it secured for him.

The Holy Family with St. Anne (63.9)

Inscribed in gilded letters around three sides of the frame with a Latin invocation of the Virgin Mary, and along the bottom part: *PETRUS PAULUS RUBENS PINXIT.* On a gold strip underneath, lower right: *NOVAR COLL.*

Canvas, *53.8 x 116.6 (60 x 45½).*

The frame is of exceptional craftsmanship and design. The outside frame is French Louis XIV, dating probably from the 1680s. The flat middle section with the inscription links the outer with the inside frame, consisting of a gilded egg-end-reel band that surrounds a narrow block molding of Dutch ripple design. The latter appears to date from the seventeenth century, but parts of it are nineteenth-century reproduction.

Provenance

Possibly the Jesuit College, Brussels, Sale 12 May 1777, No. 4A (suggested by Puyvelde).
Quinton Cranford, Paris, 1801.
Hugh Andrew Johnstone Munro, Novar, 1854-1878.
Sir Francis Cook, Doughty House, Richmond.
Sotheby's, London, 25 July 1958, lot 117; bought by J. Brent & Son, London, W.C.2.

References

J. A. Smith, *Catalogue Raisonné,* vol. II, London 1830, no. 763.
G. F. Waagen, *Treasures of Art,* vol. II, London 1854, p. 136.
M. Rooses, *L'Oeuvre de P. P. Rubens,* Antwerp 1886, vol. VI, p. 299, no. 225.
J. O. Kronig, *A Catalogue of the Paintings of Doughty House,* vol. I, London 1914, p. 83, no. 327.
R. Oldenbourg, *Rubens,* Klassiker der Kunst; Stuttgart 1921, p. 342.
L. Burchard, Letter to John Bass, 14 July 1958.

Leo van Puyvelde, *Le siècle de Rubens,* exh. cat., Brussels 1965, p. 175.
Bass Catalogue 1973, No. 9 (as Rubens).
Julius S. Held, *The Oil Sketches of Peter Paul Rubens,* vol. I, Princeton, N.J. 1980, cat. 372-73, pp. 507-8.
Julius S. Held, Letter to the Bass Museum, 11 November 1985.

Exhibitions

Brussels, Musées Royeaux des Beaux-Arts de Belgique, *Le siècle de Rubens,* October-December 1965, no. 188.

The Holy Family was a popular subject in seventeenth-century art, and Rubens and his workshop painted many variations of the theme. The Bass painting and its version in the North Carolina Museum of Art, Raleigh (Inv. 52.9.107) belong to a late phase of Rubens's career. Julius Held has traced the composition to an oil sketch by Rubens of *The Holy Family with St. Elizabeth and St. John* in the Musée des Beaux Arts, Strasbourg (fig. 1), which he dates c. 1630-1632 (ref. Held, 1980, cat. 372). This composition, and another sketch (Held, cat. 373) contain most of the elements of the figure group in the Bass picture, but the figure of St. John and the landscape on the left have been eliminated. This change makes the composition more consistently a Holy Family. The elderly woman with her arm around the Virgin's shoulder now

LAVDE·DIGNISSIMA·QVIA·EX·TE·ORTVS·E·SOL·IVSTITIÆ·✠·CHRISTVS·DEVS·NOSTER·✠

FELIX·NAMQVE·ES·SACRA·VIRGO·MARIA·ET·OMNI

PETRVS·PAVLVS·RVBENS·PINXIT

73

represents St. Anne rather than St. Elizabeth. The landscape in the Strasbourg sketch has been replaced by classical architecture. The massive pillar behind the Virgin emphasizes the central group and lends stability to the composition.

An engraving by J. Witdoeck (1615-1642), published in Rooses (see ref., vol. I, pl. 78), shows the composition in reverse (fig. 2). The parapet which supports St. Joseph has been placed at a greater distance from the pillared structure behind the Virgin, which results in greater architectural clarity. Held reports another small painted version, now in a private collection in Vancouver, which exactly corresponds (in reverse) to the Witdoeck print

(Held, 1980, p. 507). Motifs similar to those in the Bass painting can be found in several works by Rubens. The figures of the Virgin and Child are closely related to the *Holy Family with Saints* (1632-1635) in the Prado. St. Joseph and the type of architecture that supports him recall *The Education of the Virgin* (1630-1633) in the Antwerp Museum, but Joseph's pose, with his head resting on his left arm, is even more closely related to Raphael's *Madonna of Francis I* in the Louvre. Rubens also used this pose in *The Holy Family with Saint Francis* (1625-1626) at Windsor Castle. The stylistic treatment (as Haverkamp Begemann has observed) is close to the *St. Cecilia* (1639-1640) in Berlin.

Fig. 1: P. P. Rubens, *The Holy Family with St. Elizabeth and St. John.,* Strasbourg, Musée des Beaux-Arts, Inv. No. 199.

Fig. 2: *The Holy Family.* Engraving by Jean Witdoeck.

The Bass picture and its version in Raleigh have been variously ascribed to Rubens himself, to Rubens and studio, and to the studio. L. Burchard (see ref.) considered the Bass painting as a work of Rubens and of a higher quality than the Raleigh picture. Julius Held, who saw the pictures many years ago, suspects that both paintings are essentially studio pieces (ref. Held, 1985). Haverkamp Begemann, on the other hand, when seeing the Bass picture in 1986, concluded that the major part of the figures and costumes were done by Rubens, the rest by the studio (verbal information, 12 May 1986).

The excellent state of preservation and some *pentimenti* typical of Rubens (for instance, the left arm of St. Anne) add weight to the suggestion that Rubens painted essential parts of the composition himself while the studio assistants completed the work.

M.A.R.

Condition: Apart from slight retouches on the face and clothing of the Virgin and the face of the Christ Child, the painting is in very good condition throughout, painted in a sound technique that has withstood the vicissitudes of time.

PETER PAUL RUBENS, Studio

The Flight of Lot and His Family from Sodom (63.8)

Canvas, *172.7 x 228.6 (68 x 90)*.

Provenance
Collection S. del Monte, Brussels.
Bass Collection, before 1963.

References
G. Glück, *La Collection Del Monte*, Vienna 1928, cat. VI, text pp. 8-9 (as Rubens).

A. L. Mayer, "The Del Monte Collection," *Panthéon*, IV, 1929, p. 442 (as Rubens).

J. A. Goris and J. S. Held, *Rubens in America*, New York 1947, p. 31, no. 36.

R. A. d'Hulst, "Drie vroege schilderijen van Jakob Jordaens," *Gentse Bijdragen tot de kunstgeschiedenis en de oudheidskunde*, XX, 1967, p. 71.

Bass Catalogue 1973, No. 8 (as Rubens).

The National Museum of Western Art, Tokyo, *Catalogue of Paintings*, 1979, p. 195, no. 252.

F. W. Robinson and W. H. Wilson, (Catalogue of) *The Flemish and Dutch Paintings 1400-1900*, The John and Mable Ringling Museum of Art, Sarasota 1980, no. 41b (ill.).

R. A. d'Hulst, *Jacob Jordaens*, London 1982, p. 618, fig. 13.

David M. Steel, Jr., *Baroque Paintings from the Bob Jones University Collection*, exh. cat., Raleigh, N.C. 1984, p. 130, n. 3, cat. no. 40.

Julius S. Held, Letter to the Bass Museum, 11 November 1985.

R. A. d'Hulst, Letter to the Bass Museum, 27 October 1986.

Exhibitions
Budapest, *Belgian Art*, 1927, no. 10. [mentioned in Bass Catalogue 1973].
The Hague, Kunstzaal Kleykamp, 1932, no. 6.
Amsterdam, Goudstikker Gallery, 1933, no. 1.
City of Perth Art Gallery, 1940-1950.
Principal Municipal Gallery of the North of England, 1950-1951. [Mentioned in Bass Catalogue 1973].

The painting illustrates the text in Genesis (19:15-16): "When morning dawned the angels urged Lot to hurry saying: 'Arise, take your wife and your two daughters lest you be consumed in the punishment of the city.' But he lingered; so the men seized him and his wife and his two daughters by the hand, and they brought him forth and the Lord being merciful to him set him outside the city."

Rubens's composition follows this text faithfully. The frieze-like procession of the figures moves from right to left. The angel seen from behind on the left, with his fluttering draperies and outstretched arms, adds a strong directional pull which is counterbalanced by the hesitant figure of Lot placed against a massive column that marks the central axis of the picture. Lot, with flowing white beard and hair, looks back to his two daughters, who are carrying precious possessions, as if to reassure himself that they are following. The second angel is seen urging him on, and his weeping wife looks towards the desolate landscape that will soon receive them. The forward-straining body of the little dog reinforces the dynamic movement of the angel leading towards the unknown land on the left. The varied shades of red, blue, gold, and green of the garments and draperies, with their satiny sheen, lend a vibrant color harmony to the surface.

An engraving by Lucas Vorsterman, signed and dated 1620, shows the composition in reverse and bears the inscription "P. P. Rubens pinxit," and above this a dedication in Latin by Rubens to his beloved father-in-law Jan Brant.[1] The engraving leaves no doubt that Rubens painted the original of the composition, of which three versions have survived: one in the Bass Museum, another in the Ringling Museum, Sarasota, and a third in the National Museum of Western Art, Tokyo. D'Hulst and other scholars consider the Ringling version a production of the studio with Rubens's participation. The Bass version is compositionally almost identical, but its quality marks it as a studio copy. The third version, in Tokyo, is markedly different, for it shows a strong artistic personality asserting itself in the spirited brushwork, the robustness of the figures, and the vibrant light effects in the sky. The colors, too, are different from the other two versions: they are characterized by a cool brilliance and sharpness, more forceful and less harmonious than the usual Rubens palette. The artistic accomplishment of this copy has long been acknowledged by scholars who saw the painting when it was exhibited at Würzburg University (ref. Held, 1985). R. A. d'Hulst discussed the Tokyo version as a copy by Jacob Jordaens, done very soon after Rubens finished the original, c. 1613-1615 (see refs. 1967, 1982). Interestingly, the sky in the Tokyo version, with its electrifying striations of light and shade, is closer to the Vorsterman engraving than to the other two painted versions. The same is true of the landscape foreground in the Tokyo version, where a clump of grass replaces the shapeless hillock on the left of the other two paintings. The Tokyo painting may well be based on the lost original, which Vorsterman no doubt reproduced with his usual reliability. Julius Held does not accept the attribution of the Tokyo version to Jordaens.

M.A.R.

1. Henri Hymans, *Lucas Vorsterman 1595-1675, et son oeuvre gravé*, Amsterdam 1972, cat. 1.

Condition: In fair condition.

PETER PAUL RUBENS, After

Adoration of the Magi (63.10)

Panel, *39 x 28 (15¼ x 11).*

Provenance
Major Torrian.
Louis Thomas, 1864.
Countess Sala.
E.S. Bayes.
Parke-Bernet Sale, 17-18 November, 1961, lot 195 (as by
a follower of Rubens).

References
Julius Held and Jan Albert Goris, *Rubens in America,*
New York 1947, p. 50, no. A53 (as follower of Rubens).
Leo van Puyvelde, Certificate, 22 January, 1962
(as Rubens).
Bass Catalogue 1973, No. 10 (as follower of Rubens).
Julius Held, Letter to the Bass Museum, 11 November 1985
(follower of Rubens).

The composition is a copy after the monumental
painting by Rubens in St. Jean, Mechelen, or possibly
after a lost preparatory sketch. At least two other versions
of the small-scale composition are known, one in the
Metropolitan Museum, New York, and another in the
collection of the Marquis of Bute. Julius Held states
that none of these versions seems to be by the master. He
does not accept Michael Jaffe's statement that the Marquis
of Bute's version is Rubens's *modello* for the St. Jean
altarpiece (Held, 1985).[1]

The Bass picture is painted with a lightness of
touch and a sensitivity that point to an artist of the
eighteenth century.

M.A.R.

1. Michael Jaffe, "Rediscovered Oil Sketches by Rubens," *Burlington Magazine,* July 1969, p. 435f., fig. 29.

Condition: Apart from one major split through the Magi's red robe, the thin cradled panel is in exceptionally good condition. Thin sketchy application of paint with some abrasions and a few retouches, for instance in the Christ Child's forehead.

SEBASTIANO DEL PIOMBO, After

Italian, 1485-1547

Sebastiano del Piombo (born Sebastiani Luciani) received his training in Venice from Giorgione. After his master's death in 1510, he moved to Rome where he spent the remainder of his life. He worked alongside Raphael and Peruzzi in the decoration of the Villa Farnesina and received many commissions for altarpieces and portraits. After Raphael's death in 1520, Sebastiano became the most important painter in Rome. In 1531 his artistic labors were rewarded by the Pope, who made him keeper of the seal (or *piombo*) of the Curia. Thereafter he did little painting until his death in 1547.

The Madonna of the Veil (63.23)

Canvas, *130 x 107 (51 x 40).*

Provenance
Volterra Gallery, Florence.
Art Institute, Minneapolis.
Bass Collection, before 1963.

References
Bass Catalogue 1973, No. 23 (as Sebastiano del Piombo).

The Bass *Madonna of the Veil* is a faithful sixteenth-century copy of a work painted by Sebastiano for Pope Clement VII in 1525, today in the Narodni Galerie, Prague. Sebastiano's *Madonna of the Veil* was directly inspired by the example of Raphael's painting of the same subject (Chantilly, Musée Condé) of c. 1509-1510, which originally hung in the Roman church of Santa Maria del Popolo.[1] (The sleeping Christ Child reflects, in reverse, the winged putto beneath Raphael's *Galatea* at the Villa Farnesina, Rome).[2] The meaning of Sebastiano's version, however, is quite different from that of Raphael's.[3] In Sebastiano's painting the Christ Child is about to be covered by his mother with a thin veil and is shown sleeping, not awake as in Raphael's. Moreover He grasps a sparrow in one hand. The Infant St. John the Baptist, absent from the earlier version by Raphael, stands alongside the Madonna and holds in his hand a staff with a banderole inscribed with the word "Agnus" (lamb). John the Baptist's presence thus calls attention to the Christ Child's role as the sacrificial lamb whose sacrifice allowed for the salvation of even the lowliest of mankind's souls (symbolized by the sparrow). In using the image of the Virgin watching over the sleeping Christ Child as a reference to the Passion, Sebastiano introduced into Roman High Renaissance painting an iconographic tradition employed by Northern Italian artists since the late fourteenth century.[4]

P.L.R.

1. M. Hirst, *Sebastiano del Piombo,* Oxford 1981, p. 85.
2. Ibid.
3. Ibid.
4. Ibid.

Condition: The painting was relined at an unknown date. The condition is uneven.

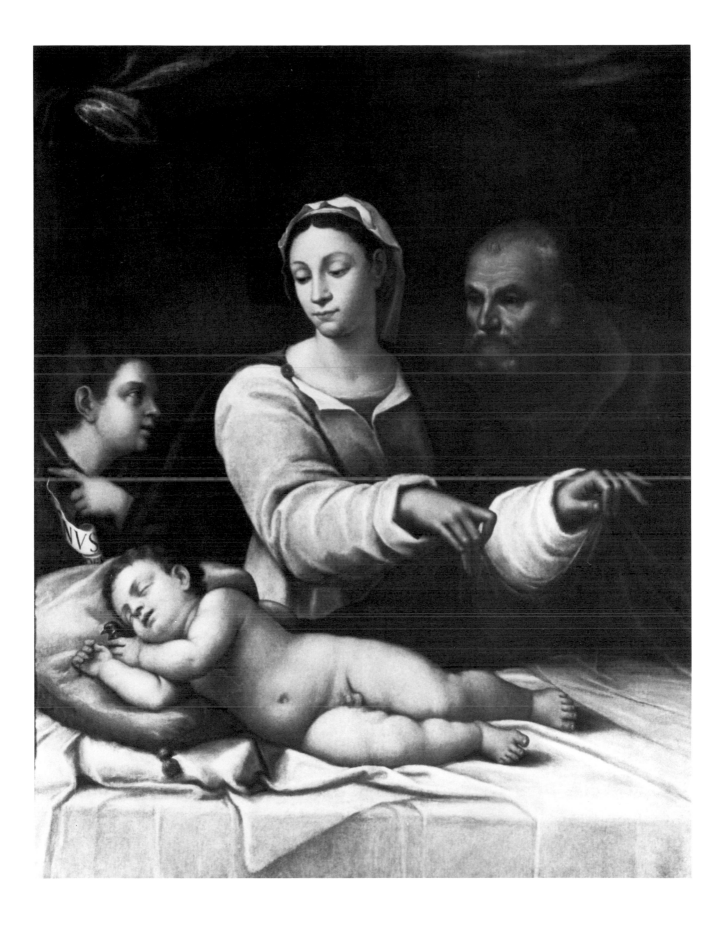

GERARD SEGHERS

Flemish, 1591-1651

Born in Antwerp, Gerard was the younger brother of Daniel Seghers and a pupil of Abraham Janssens. Like his master he became a portrait and history painter and was accepted as Master of the Guild in 1608. After travels to Rome and Madrid, he settled in Antwerp in 1620. Initially he worked in the Caravaggesque manner, but in the later 1620s he became a follower and frequent collaborator of Rubens. After Rubens's death Gerard Seghers became one of the most prominent and wealthy painters in Antwerp. His works are in many churches and museums.

Christ and the Penitents (63.15)

Canvas, *167.6 x 231 (66 x 91).*

Provenance

Lucien Bonaparte, Prince de Oanino.
The Rev. Charles Wheeler, acquired in Paris, 1834.
Mrs. Wheeler, Otterdam Place, Faversham, Kent.
Bass Collection, 1963.

References

B. Renckens, Netherlands Institute for Art History,
The Hague, Letter to John Bass, 22 October 1959.
Bass Catalogue 1973, No. 15.
Julius S. Held, Letter to M. Russell, 11 November 1985.

The composition focuses on the figure of Christ standing left of center, holding the cross in his left arm and looking full face towards the beholder. Christ is surrounded by a group of sinners who are known to have repented and by other figures: on the right the Good Thief, King David with his harp, and the Magdalen, and on the left the Prodigal Son with one of the pigs he tended, and the Publican.

The theme of Christ among the sinners had been treated in Netherlandish painting at least since 1560. It was a subject favored by the Counter Reformation and hence mainly confined to the southern Netherlands, although there are a few examples in Dutch painting. The sinners represented in such paintings vary, but the most beloved of repentant sinners, the Magdalen, is almost always included. The iconography of the Bass painting is most closely related to an altarpiece by Otto van Veen (now in Mainz), where Christ is shown with the same personages.[1] Another painting by Seghers of the same subject, but showing the Magdalen kneeling before Christ, is in the Rijksmuseum, Amsterdam (A374).[2] The pictorial treatment, based on three-quarter-length life-size figures whose volume fills most of the picture space, is derived from Caravaggio and characteristic of much of Southern Baroque painting.

The attribution of the Bass picture to Seghers was first made by Julius Held and confirmed by the Netherlands Institute for Art History, The Hague (see refs.).

M.A.R.

1. John B. Knipping, *Iconography of the Counter-Reformation in the Netherlands,* Nieuwkoop/Leiden 1974, vol. II, p. 316. Knipping discusses many other paintings and engravings illustrating the subject of Christ and the Sinners.
2. Ibid.

Condition: In fair condition. Faces are in good condition with some retouches. Christ's body shows areas of loss and overpaint.

SPANISH SCHOOL (Aragonese), Attributed to

Fifteenth century

Retable (63.37)

Tempera on panel, overall *198.7 x 158.3 (77½ x 59).*
The panel is 3.8 cm. thick and consists of at least three
sections. The major square part has six painted scenes; it
rests on a predella with four small paintings and is topped
by a painted pediment.

Provenance
Said to come from a church at Calatayud.
Conde de las Almenas, Madrid.
Eric de Kolb, New York.

References
C.R. Post, *A History of Spanish Painting,* vol. XIII,
Harvard University Press 1966, p. 253, fig. 99.
Bass Catalogue 1973, No. 37.

The composition is dominated by the seated figure of an
unidentified bishop-saint, flanked by Sts. Cosmas (left)
and Damian (right). The upper tier shows on the left the
bishop preaching, and on the right stretched out on his
deathbed. The center panel has a scene of the Crucifixion.
The heads of Christ and two angels are painted in the
pediment. The predella panels feature, from left to right,
St. James Major, the Virgin Mary, the Risen Christ, and
St. John the Evangelist. A panel with St. Anthony Abbot
has been lost and replaced with the carved panel in the
center, where originally the figure of Christ was placed
(ref. Post).

Post (see ref.) lists the retable under 'Uncertain
Attributions' and remarks that its best feature is the
nicely carved and gilded Plateresque frame.

M.A.R.

Condition: An old retouched split runs across the center section, through the figure of Christ and the face of the seated bishop below. The carved panel with
cherubs' heads and 'palm-trunk' colonettes in the center of the predella is a later addition, probably sixteenth century. The panel is in poor condition, with
flakings and abrasions throughout. The Plateresque frame is of superior workmanship. It has been regilded and the bottom right section replaced.

BERNHARD STRIGEL, Workshop or Circle of

German (Swabian), 1460-1528

Born in Memmingen, a prosperous city southeast of Ulm, Bernhard Strigel represented the third generation of a well-established family of artists. He carried on the family tradition as head of a large workshop of painters and sculptors who supplied altarpieces to the local churches and portraits to the patricians. Bernhard's success carried him beyond his local position: the Emperor Maximilian I appointed him as a court painter. His native city held him in high esteem and repeatedly sent him as its delegate for negotiations with neighboring cities. His most important mission was to the imperial court at Innsbruck to secure the repayment of a large loan to the city.

Stylistically, Strigel achieved the transition from the late Gothic tradition to the German Renaissance with its new 'realism' inspired by Italian art and by contacts with the Netherlands. His frequent travels involved a dependence on well-trained assistants in the workshop. The collaboration of his son-in-law and of a *knecht* (assistant) is occasionally acknowledged in documents.

Two panels of an altarpiece:
The Holy Kinship (63.21 and 63.22)

Painted *c. 1490 - 1500.*

Panel, *110 x 83 (42½ x 32½)* each.

Provenance
Bass Collection, 1963.

References
Dr. Ludwig Beldass, Certificate, n.d. (as circle of Hans Multscher).
Bass Catalogue 1973, Nos. 21, 22 (quoting Beldass's attribution).

The Holy Kinship was a popular subject for painting in Germany during the fifteenth and sixteenth centuries. According to the *Trinubium* legend, as told in Jacobus de Voragine's well-known *Golden Legend,* Anna, mother of the Virgin Mary, had been married three times, to (1) Joachim, (2) Cleophas, and (3) Salome. The Virgin Mary was born from the first marriage, Mary Cleophas from the second, and Mary Salome from the third (she was the mother of St. John the Evangelist). Anna and the three Marys became a popular subject for painting from the fourteenth century onwards. Eventually Anna's three husbands, as well as the husbands and children of the three Marys, were included in several compositions to form an enlarged group usually referred to as the Holy Kinship *(Heilige Sippe).*

The Bass panels represent such an enlarged group. Anna, the Virgin Mary, and the Christ Child are featured on the left; Anna's three husbands are standing behind her, with Joachim placed prominently in the center. On the right behind the Virgin is the figure of Joseph. On the right panel are Mary Cleophas, reading a book, with her husband Alphaeus and their four children: James the Minor, Joseph the Just, Simon, and Jude. To the right of this group are Mary Salome with her husband Zebedee

and their children: John the Evangelist, (identified by his attributes, the eagle and the book) and James the Greater (holding his pilgrim's staff, for he went as a pilgrim to Spain, and an apple, symbol of the redemption through Christ's Passion). The Christ Child, on the panel opposite, holds an apple in each hand, alluding to the same symbolism.

The Bass panels were previously attributed to the circle of Hans Multscher (1400-1469), who also worked in Ulm but whose style is typical of an earlier generation. All the stylistic evidence points to an artist close to Bernhard Strigel who was perhaps also influenced by Bertholomé Zeitblom of Ulm (1455/60-1518/22), a frequent collaborator with Strigel.[1] Bernhard Strigel and his workshop often painted the subject of the Holy Kinship. Their most famous example was on the verso of the master's group portrait of *The Emperor Maximillian and his Family* in the Kunsthistorische Museum, Vienna (cat. 1958, no. 573/74; the verso religious scene has now been separated from the portrait).

M.A.R.

1. The connection with Strigel and Zeitblom was recognized by Larry Silver, to whom I am indebted for suggesting our new attribution.

Condition: The panels are heavily overpainted and the bottom strip of the right panel is an old replacement.

TITIAN, After

Italian, 1490-1576

Titian (born Tiziano Vecellio) was one of the most outstanding Venetian painters of the sixteenth century, who in the course of his sixty-year career attained a European-wide reputation. He was born at Pieve di Cadore outside of Venice, but trained in the city with Giovanni Bellini (active c. 1460-1516) and subsequently with Giorgione (1478?-1510). Titian's first major commissions were frescos for the Fondaco dei Tedeschi (today the Galeria Franchetti) in Venice, around 1508, and for the Scuola del Santo in Padua in 1511. By the mid 1520s he had established his reputation as a painter of innovative religious altarpieces with two works for the church of the Frari, Venice (the *Frari Assumption,* 1516-1518, and the *Pesaro Madonna,* 1519-1526); he was recognized equally as a master of mythological *poesie* for three paintings executed between 1518 and 1523 for the *Camerino d'Alabastro* of Alfonso d'Este, Duke of Ferrara (*Bacchus and Ariadne,* now in the National Gallery, London, and *The Andrians* and *The Worship of Venus,* in the Prado, Madrid). Throughout the 1530s and 40s, Titian was extremely prolific, producing many important religious and mythological works, as well as portraits including those of Federico Gonzaga, Duke of Urbino, and his wife Eleonora, the Holy Roman Emperor Charles V, and Pope Paul III. From the 1550s until his death in 1576 Titian's major patron was Philip II of Spain.

The Three Ages of Man (63.27)

Canvas, *93.6 x 148.7 (36½ x 58).*

The painting probably has its original frame which is of sixteenth-century manufacture in the Sansovino style. It may then have had a coat-of-arms on the central lozenge.

Provenance

Collection Manfrin, Venice.
Collection Alexander Barker, London.
Collection Lord Dudley, London.
Christie's, London, Dudley Sale, 25 June 1892, No. 66.
Collection G.O. Farrer, Sandhurst Lodge, England.
Sotheby's, London, Sale, 5 February 1947.
Bass Collection, before 1963.

References

B. Berenson, *Italian Pictures of the Renaissance, Venetian School,* London 1957, vol. I, p. 143 (attributed to Polidoro Lanzani).
H. Wethey, *The Paintings of Titian: The Mythological Paintings,* London 1957, vol. 3, p. 184 (copy 7).
Bass Catalogue 1973, No. 27 (as Polidoro Lanzano [Lanciano] [sic]).

Exhibitions

London, Royal Academy of Art, 1852.
London, Venetian Exhibition, New Gallery, 1894-1895.

Among the early works by Titian which most clearly display his debt to the style and content of Giorgione's work is the *Three Ages of Man* (Edinburgh, Sutherland Loan) of c. 1511-1517. The painting is an allegory emphasizing the beauty of life when love is young, but with a reminder of the inevitability of death.[1] On the right side of the painting are two babies (symbolizing Infancy) sleeping beneath a dead tree-trunk and protected from harm and possible death by an attendant cupid. To the left are two young lovers (representing Maturity) who gaze passionately into one another's eyes. They hold in their hands recorders, symbolic of their amorous union and the harmony of their souls.[2] Seated far back in the bucolic landscape which serves as the setting for the allegory is an elderly man holding two skulls, representing Old Age and Death. Although the conception of the work was certainly dependent upon beliefs associated with the Golden Age of Antiquity, there is no exact prototype in classical literature for the sentiment illustrated by Titian in this painting; moreover, the iconography of the work was undoubtedly Titian's own creation.[3]

Like many of Titian's paintings, the *Three Ages of Man* was copied on a number of occasions in the course of the sixteenth century. The two best copies are those in the Villa Borghese and the Doria Pamphili collections, Rome.[4] The Bass version is a free, late-sixteenth-century copy (probably of the Doria Pamphili painting),[5] distinguishable from the original by a number of variations, especially in the handling of the figures.

The painting has been ascribed in the past to Polidoro Lanzani (Berenson) and to Paolo Veronese (Bass Museum file); however there is no evidence to support either attribution.

P.L.R.

1. H. Wethey, *The Paintings of Titian: The Mythological Paintings,* London 1971, vol. 3, p. 17.
2. Ibid., p. 18.
3. Ibid., p. 18.
4. Ibid., pp. 183-84.
5. Ibid., p. 184.

Condition: Overpainting and abrasion throughout. The retouches have discolored.

TITIAN, AFTER

Madonna and Child with St. Luke and a Donor (63.13)

Canvas, *129.5 x 171.2 (50½ x 66¾).*
The frame is French, from the eighteenth century, in the Louis XV style; it has been enlarged to fit the painting.

Provenance
Collection of Miss Young, Grange-over-Sands, England.
Christie's, London, Sale 3 July 1953, No. 26; bought by Hallsborough (see ref. Wethey).
Bass Collection, before 1963.

References
H. Wethey, *The Paintings of Titian: The Religious Paintings,* London 1971, p. 107 (copy 2).
Bass Catalogue 1973, No. 13 (as Anthony van Dyck).

Among the many outstanding works painted by Titian in the late years of his prolific career is the *Madonna and Child with Sts. Catherine and Luke* (Kreuzlingen, Heinz Kisters) of c. 1560. In the right half of the painting, the Madonna is shown seated (almost in profile), facing towards the left, with the frolicsome Christ Child in her lap; kneeling at her feet, is St. Catherine who reaches to touch the outstretched arm of the squirming infant. Behind her, to the left, stands St. Luke, holding his Gospel. The three-quarter-length figures are silhouetted against a far distant landscape which is partially blocked from view by a curtain suspended behind the head of the Virgin. A variant of this composition (Hampton Court, England), perhaps painted by a pupil of Titian, shows the kneeling figure of St. Catherine replaced with that of a male donor and adds to St. Luke his traditional attribute, the ox. The Bass painting of the *Madonna and Child with St. Luke and a Donor* is one of two known copies of this variant composition (see ref. Wethey). The painting has been ascribed in the past to Anthony van Dyck (Bass Catalogue 1973) and to Lambert Sustris (Bass Museum file); however there is no evidence to support either attribution.

P.L.R.

Condition: Uneven condition, with various abrasions and retouchings.

JAN WEENIX

Dutch, 1640-1719

Like his father, Jan Baptist Weenix, and his cousin Melchior d'Hondecouter, Jan Weenix specialized in hunting still-lifes, with dead game and birds, which were extremely popular in the second half of the seventeenth century. His subjects were usually depicted in a park-like setting resplendent with richly carved ornamental sculpture. Weenix worked in Utrecht and Amsterdam, and from 1702 to c. 1716 he was employed by the Elector Palatine at Düsseldorf to decorate the castle of Benberg with hunting scenes on a monumental scale.

Lady Playing the Viola (79.183)

Painted 1713.

Previously inscribed on the base of the stone vase:
J. Weenix 1713; inscription no longer visible.

Canvas, *179.5 x 141 (70 x 55)*.

Provenance
Palais Galliera, Paris, Sale 30 March 1963, no. 30.
Heim S. A., Paris.
Purchased by the Bass Collection 3 September 1966.

References
Catalogue Palais Galliera, 30 March 1963, no. 30, with illustration.
Rebecca J. Ginnings, *The Art of Jan Baptist Weenix and Jan Weenix*, unpublished Ph.D. dissertation, University of Delaware, 1970, cat. no. 129, fig. 127.
Bass Catalogue 1973, No. 183.
François Heim (Heim S. A.), Letter to the Bass Museum, 30 October 1985.
Peter C. Sutton, *Dutch Art in America*, Grand Rapids 1986, p. 153.

When Weenix turned to portraiture late in his career, he liked to pose his sitters in the same outdoor setting that he used for his hunting still-lifes. The elegant young lady here portrayed against such a background is represented in the popular form of an allegory of music. Her costume and hairstyle are of a type that became fashionable in the early eighteenth century, after 1710.[1] Hence the picture must date from the last years of the artist's life (the date on the lost inscription, 1713, seems exactly right).

Jan Weenix's portraiture was influenced by the late portraits of Nicolaes Maes and Caspar Netscher. Like them, he aimed at the aristocratic elegance of the court of Versailles under Louis XIV, which set the trends in art and fashion throughout Europe.

Classical sculpture and architecture, as well as dogs, birds, fruit, and flowers, are frequently included in Weenix's portraits. A large ornamental urn of the type seen in the Bass painting is almost invariably present as a foil for the figures. The picture, with its life-size stylish figure and sumptuous setting, fits well into the aristocratic environment of the court at Düsseldorf, where it was most probably painted.

M.A.R.

1. Verbal communication by R. Ginsberg, Curator of Costumes, Victoria & Albert Museum, London.

Condition: Cleaned in 1963/64 by Galerie Heim, Paris, when the inscription of the artist's name and date disappeared; the style and character of the painting, however, suggest that the signature and date were genuine. E. Haverkamp Begemann suggested that the painting might have been signed over the varnish; he knows a similar case where the artist's father, Jan Baptist Weenix, had signed his name over the varnish (verbal communication, May 12, 1986). Good condition.

BENJAMIN WEST, P.R.A.

American, 1738-1820

B orn at Springfield, Pennsylvania, Benjamin West received basic art training in Philadelphia before leaving in 1760 to tour Italy for three years. He settled in London in 1763 and attracted the favor of King George III, especially as a history painter. Among his many history paintings, *The Death of Wolfe* (1771) is perhaps his masterpiece. West was the first American painter to achieve international fame. He was elected a foundation member of the Royal Academy in 1768 and succeeded Sir Joshua Reynolds as president in 1792.

Anne, Countess of Northampton, with Her Daughter Elizabeth (63.32)

Signed and dated lower left: *B. West/ Venice/ 1762.*
Inscribed lower left: *B. West.*
Canvas, *130.7 x 105.2 (51 x 41).*

Provenance
Collection of Henry F. C. Cavendish, 1905.
Christie's, London, 7 April 1933, lot 135, and again 26 May 1933, lot 18.
Anderson Galleries, New York, 17-18 May 1934, lot 137.
Minneapolis Institute of Arts, 1945 (given by Chester Dale).
Julius Weitzner, New York and London, 1958.
Bass Museum, 1963.

References
Catalogue of Portraits, Miniatures etc. in the Possession of Cecil George Savile, 4th Earl of Liverpool, 1905, p. 33, no. 2.
"A West Portrait of the Italian Period," *Bulletin of the Minneapolis Institute of Arts,* XXXIV, 1945, pp. 96-101.
Helmut von Erffa, "Benjamin West: The Early Years in London," *American Art Journal,* V, 1973, pp. 4-14.
Bass Catalogue 1973, No. 32.
Robert C. Alberts, *Benjamin West: A Biography,* Boston 1978, p. 50.
Helmut von Erffa and Allen Staley, *The Paintings of Benjamin West,* New Haven, 1986, cat. no. 676, text p. 19, color ill. p. 18.

Exhibitions
The Baltimore Museum of Art, June to August 1989, no. 4.

Anne, Countess of Northampton (1740/41-1763), was born Lady Anne Somerset, the eldest daughter of the 4th Duke of Beaufort. In 1759 she married Charles Compton, 7th Earl of Northampton. Their daughter Lady Elizabeth Compton was born in 1760. Lord Northampton was appointed Ambassador Extraordinary and Plenipotentiary to Venice in August 1762. He arrived with his family in October and West must have painted the Countess and her daughter very soon afterwards. They are posed as a Madonna and Child with clear reference to compositions by Raphael, in particular the *Madonna del Granduca* and the *Madonna della Sedia.* According to an entry in the 1905 catalogue of paintings in the collection of Lord Liverpool (see ref.), the Bass painting was at that time owned by Henry F. C. Cavendish, while Lord Liverpool owned a copy.

In 1782, the year of her marriage to Lord Henry Augustus Cavendish, Lady Elizabeth (the child in the Bass painting) was painted at full-length by Sir Joshua Reynolds. This fine portrait is now in the National Gallery of Art, Washington, D. C. Her husband was created Earl of Burlington in 1831.

K.J.G./M.A.R.

Condition: Cleaned in 1988. Excellent condition. The Maratta style (Italian) frame appears to be contemporary with the painting.

HENRY WYATT

British, 1794-1840

The portrait and genre painter Henry Wyatt was born near Lichfield in the Midlands but came to London early and entered the Royal Academy schools in 1812, moving to the studio of Sir Thomas Lawrence in 1815 as a pupil and rapidly being promoted to assistant. In 1817 he began to practice independently, moving around the country and finally, in 1825, settling at Leamington Spa. Wyatt's work is mostly small scale. His genre pictures, with titles like *Curiosity* or *Naughty Pet,* have the charm of the drawing-room albums of the period.

Portrait of a Lady (Lady Grantham?) (79.250)

Canvas, *76.4 x 64.1 (25¼ x 30⅛).*

Provenance
Edith S. Breyer (estate of).
Parke-Bernet Galleries, New York, 3 November 1967, lot 78 (as *Lady Grantham),* purchased for The Bass Collection.

References
Bass Catalogue 1973, No. 250.

The picture has been traditionally called a portrait of Lady Grantham (1784-1848), a daughter of the 1st Earl of Inniskillen, who married Thomas Philip, 3rd Lord Grantham, in 1805. He succeeded to the titles of Earl de Grey and Baron Lucas in 1833 and died in 1859 when the Grantham title went to his brother. It is now extinct. Lady Grantham was painted by Lawrence in 1814 when she was thirty, which may be the approximate age of the sitter in Wyatt's portrait, but the likeness between the sitters in the two portraits is slight. Moreover the dress and style in the Wyatt portrait point to a later date.

K.J.G.

Condition: Good condition.

OTTO BARTH

Austrian, 1876-1916

O tto Barth was born in Vienna and studied first in a private drawing academy and later at the Akademie der Bildenden Künste in Vienna. From 1907 to 1912, he was a member of the Hagenbund, a 'moderately modern' association of Viennese artists who took an intermediary position between the conservative Künstlerhaus and the progressive Secession. Barth was a friend of the painter Oscar Laske whose portrait by Pick-Morino is in the Bass Collection (No. 79.209). He painted landscapes and was particularly fond of mountain scenery, which he also represented in lithographs and in designs for ceramic tiles.

Two Skiers in the Mountains (79.198)

Signed lower right: *Otto Barth.*
Painted c. 1908.
Canvas, *111.8 x 145.4 (44 x 57¼).*
Inscription on back: *Matthias Zdarsky auf der Rax.*

Provenance
Kunsthandlung Karl Löscher/Anton Jancsy, Vienna.
Purchased for the Bass Collection 25 July 1966.

References
Bass Catalogue 1973, No. 198.

Exhibitions
Vienna, Künstlerbund Hagen, 1908, no. 13 (?).

Barth exhibited a picture called *Die Bergführer* (The Mountain Guides) in the Hagenbund exhibition of 1908. This picture is probably identical with the Bass Museum painting. Many Viennese painters around 1900 concentrated on the subject of winter landscape. They were attracted by the special mood and the challenge of a restricted palette inherent in snow scenes.

The picture includes a portrait of Matthias Zdarsky (1856-1940); however, it is not clear which of the two figures represents him. Zdarsky was a pioneer of alpine skiing. In 1897, he wrote the first skiing instruction book, *Die alpine Schifahr-Technik* (Alpine Skiing Technique). He came from Lilienfeld in Austria, where a small museum, the Zdarsky Museum, keeps his memory alive. The Rax is a mountain range situated approximately eighty kilometers southwest of Vienna.

G.F.

GYULIA BENCZUR

Hungarian, 1844-1920

Benczur was born on 16 July 1844 in Nyiregyhaza (Hungary) and he died on 16 July 1920 in Dolany (today CSSR), which was renamed Benczurfalva after the artist's death. In 1861, Benczur began his studies at the Munich Academy, where he first exhibited in 1864. From 1865 to 1869 he studied with one of the most famous history painters of his time, Karl von Piloty (who was also the teacher of Hans Makart). Benczur made his name as an independent artist with the painting of a scene from Hungarian history (*The Farewell of Laszlo Hunyadi*). A stay in Paris, 1875, was followed by a journey to Venice, 1876. On his return Benczur was appointed a professor at the Academy of Munich. In 1883 he returned to Hungary, where he was successful as an artist and educator. He became one of the most popular portraitists of the Hungarian aristocracy and also painted several members of the Austrian Imperial Family. His international fame was founded on his numerous history paintings. In contrast with his Vienna colleague Hans Makart he strived at a sensitive realization of historical truth. Paintings by Benczur are to be found in the Hungarian National Gallery in Budapest, in the Neue Pinakothek and in the Städtische Galerie, Lenbachhaus, in Munich.

Louis XVI and Marie Antoinette with Their Children at Versailles, October 6, 1789 (79.274)

Signed and dated on lower right: *Benczur Gyula, Munchen 1872.*

Canvas, *143 x 213 (57 x 85).*

Provenance
Parke-Bernet, New York, 27 November 1968, lot 243.

References
F. v. Boetticher, *Malerwerke des 19. Jahrhunderts,* Vol. I/1, Dresden 1891, p. 74, no. 3.
U. Thieme and F. Becker, *Allgemeines Lexikon der Bildenden Künstler von der Antike bis zur Gegenwart,* vol. III, Leipzig 1909, p. 289.

The scene described by the painter shows the moment shortly before the rebels break through the door in order to force the King and his family to leave Versailles for the royal city palace, the Tuíleries. Louis had joined the French Revolution under duress and could not reconcile himself with his role as constitutional monarch. On 21 September 1792 he was dethroned, and on 21 January 1793 he died with his wife on the guillotine. He had married Marie Antoinette, a daughter of the Empress Maria Theresia, in 1770.

Benczur skillfully dramatized the scene through his realization of the various characters and their reactions. The King, resigned and irresolute, is slumped in a chair. His figure appears emotionally separated from the group of women and children. The highlight on theatrical aspects in this painting bears witness to the influence of Piloty. Benczur's history paintings were mostly devoted to subjects from French and Hungarian history.

G.F.

Arnold Clementschitsch

Austrian, 1887-1970.

Born in Villach, Carinthia, Arnold Clementschitsch received his education as an artist in Vienna, from 1909 to 1911, and then in Munich until 1915. From 1918 he lived in Villach, but stayed in France in 1933-34. Between 1917 and 1925, Clementschitsch painted many urban scenes which were influenced by late French Impressionism. Later he concentrated on landscape, and from 1935 he painted mainly portraits. He was also a writer and published books, among them a volume of poetry.

Self-Portrait (79.201)

Signed lower right: *Clementschitsch.*
Painted c. 1910.
Canvas, *38.5 x 32.7 (15 x 12¾).*

Provenance
Kunsthandlung Karl Löscher/Anton Jancsy, Vienna.
Purchased for the Bass Collection 25 July 1966.

References
Bass Catalogue 1973, No. 201.

Exhibitions
Graz, Künstlerhaus, January/February 1966, no. 15.

In 1920, Clementschitsch exhibited for the first time outside his immediate vicinity, namely on the premises of the artists' society Secession in Vienna. This event marked the beginning of a promising career. The self-portrait must have been painted shortly before. With its lavish impasto and strong visible brushstrokes, the painting is typical of the artist's early period and also of this relatively early phase of Austrian Expressionism.

G.F.

EUGÈNE DELACROIX, Attributed to

French, 1798-1863

Delacroix was the acknowledged leader of the Romantic school of painting in nineteenth-century France. His delight in color and movement owed much to his admiration for the great Baroque master Peter Paul Rubens, some of whose paintings he copied in the Louvre. His style was in conflict with the classicism of David and Ingres and he was considered by academic circles a revolutionary artist. He was not accepted as a member of the Institut de France until 1857; however, his genius dominated the artistic scene in France. His *Journals*, covering the years from 1823 to 1854, are an invaluable record of the life of the painter and his period.

The Kermesse (after Peter Paul Rubens) (64.109)

Painted c. 1850-1860.
Canvas, *61 x 77.5 (23³⁄₈ x 30½).*

Provenance
Collection of Sir David White.

References
Bass Catalogue 1973, No. 109.
Lee Johnson, Letter to the Bass Museum, 1985.

The picture is a faithful copy after Rubens's *Kermesse* in the Louvre. It seems to have been cut a few centimeters on the left, and a little less on the right margin, thus eliminating from the Rubens composition one female figure on the far left and most of the hut and the tree on the right.

Two other nineteenth-century copies of the *Kermesse* are known. Both are attributed to Daumier and reproduced in Maison, figs. B and C.[1] Copy C (private collection, Geneva) is a free adaptation of Rubens's composition, changing and omitting several motifs. Copy B however, which was destroyed by fire in 1953, follows the Rubens composition faithfully in all details, and so does the Bass copy (with the exception of the losses on left and right). Copy B, judging from the photograph, shows all the characteristics of Daumier's style, although Maison declares himself as "not fully convinced but inclined to believe it."[2]

The Bass picture has recently been examined by Dr. Paula Harper, who was the first to recognize its connection with the Daumier copies. She judged that it could not be by Daumier himself but seems to be by an artist close to Daumier. The Bass picture, though compositionally identical with copy B, is executed in a much more painterly manner than Daumier's copies, where all figures are rendered in the sharply delineated contours typical of the artist's draftsman-like technique. The Bass picture, with its painterly fluid brushwork, follows more closely the manner of Rubens and is stylistically closer to Delacroix

than to Daumier. Hence the tentative attribution to Delacroix in the 1973 Bass Museum Catalogue seems not unjustified.

According to records, Delacroix took a great interest in Rubens's *Kermesse* and he may have been the artist who drew Daumier's attention to the picture. Adhémar reports that Daumier, when frequenting the Flemish gallery at the Louvre in c. 1846-1847, would "encounter Delacroix in front of the *Kermesse* by Rubens."[3] Delacroix himself expressed his admiration for the Rubens picture in his *Journal*, 11 October 1852: "As to the golden highlight... it has a fine quality: Rubens uses it everywhere... it is written into the Kermess."[4]

A recent tentative suggestion that the Bass picture might be a twentieth-century copy by the Swedish painter L. Reis, who owned Daumier's copy B before it was burned, is ruled out by the restorer's report. The condition of the paint and the lining are consistent with an origin in the nineteenth century.[5]

The Delacroix scholar Lee Johnson, on seeing a photograph of the Bass picture, rejected the attribution to Delacroix, but he did not seem to be aware that the picture is a copy after Rubens nor that Delacroix took an interest in the Rubens *Kermesse* (see ref. Johnson). The Bass *Kermesse* is painted with considerable verve. A recent study of Delacroix's copies after Rubens in the Louvre by M. Russell supports the probability of Delacroix's authorship. Jacques Foucart, who has published on the

subject of copies after Rubens,[6] agreed that Delacroix is most likely the artist of the Bass painting.

Barbara Ehrlich White in her article on Delacroix's painted copies after Rubens (*Art Bulletin,* March 1967, p. 37ff.) does not mention this copy, the existence of which would have been unknown to her. She states that "in most cases Delacroix's painting {i.e. copy} is considerably smaller than its prototype. All {copies} seem to have been made for Delacroix's own pleasure or instruction, and none of them is signed and dated." The Bass picture is indeed considerably smaller than the Rubens *Kermesse* and is unsigned and undated.

1. K. E. Maison, *Honoré Daumier, Catalogue Raisonné of the Paintings, Watercolors and Drawings,* Greenwich, Connecticut, 1968, vol. 1, p. 213.
2. Ibid.
3. Jean Adhémar, *Honóre Daumier,* Paris 1954, pp. 33, 115, cat. 27. Adhémar reproduces only Maison's copy C, which he attributes without hesitation to Daumier.
4. *The Journal of Eugène Delacroix,* tr. by Walter Peach, New York 1948, p. 278. Delacroix was referring to highlights of Naples yellow, which he was using at the time for the ceiling in the Salon de la Paix.
5. Rustin Levenson, Report on *The Kermesse,* Bass Museum No. 64.109, June 1986.
6. Jacques Foucart, "Rubens: Copies, repliques, pastiches," *Revue de l'Art,* 1973, no. 21.

M.A.R.

Condition: Canvas probably reduced on left end right. In good condition. The paint surface, done in a wet-on-wet technique, has few age cracks. The lining is old. The condition of the painting is consistent with an origin in the nineteenth century.

LEO DELITZ

Austrian, 1882-1966

Born in Zagreb (today in Yugoslavia), Leo Delitz studied at the Vienna Academy from 1898 to 1904, and then in Munich and Paris. He lived in Vienna but undertook many journeys to Italy, France, Holland, Russia, and Egypt. During the First World War he worked as a war artist. In 1938 he emigrated to England. Delitz was mainly occupied with portraiture.

Slovakian Girl (79.254)

Signed lower right: *L. Delitz.*
Canvas, *114.1 x 100 (44½ x 39).*

Provenance
Bass Collection, 1967.

References
Bass Catalogue 1973, No. 254.

Delitz skillfully exploits the interplay between the varied colors of the girl's dress and the blossoms of the bower. The painting follows a fashionable trend in the visual arts of Vienna, c. 1900, to make use of folk designs, as in this instance the colorful Slovak pattern of the fabric.

Throughout his life, the painter excelled in unconventional portrait compositions and remained faithful to the clear pastel shades here employed.

G.F.

JULES DUPRÉ

French, 1811-1889

Originally trained in the art of porcelain decoration, Jules Dupré later became a landscape painter and lithographer. A trip to England in 1834 proved to be a turning point in his career, for it brought him into contact with the art of John Constable. Constable's fresh approach to nature greatly influenced the body of Dupré's work. During the 1830s and 1840s, he joined Théodore Rousseau and the group of painters of the Barbizon School, painting outdoor scenery in the forest of Fontainebleau. Although Dupré, along with other members of the Barbizon School, abandoned the academic technique of landscape painting, he was a respected and frequent contributor to the Paris salons. The Legion of Honor was awarded to him in 1849.

Barbizon Landscape (79.267)

Signed lower left: *Jules Dupré.*
Canvas, *92.3 x 151.3 (36 x 59).*

Provenance
Plaza Art Gallery, New York.
Purchased for the Bass Collection, 14 December 1967.

Reference
Bass Catalogue 1973, No. 267.

Exhibitions
Montgomery, Alabama, Museum of Fine Arts, September 1988-February 1989, Catalogue, p. 22.

This fine landscape combines the realism of the Barbizon School with a more romantic concept of nature which the artist developed late in his career. A pyramidal mass of trees with brooding shadows reminiscent of Bocklin's mystical landscapes rises in the center. Drifting clouds in the silvery sky and their shadows on the fields below, alternating with brightly sunlit patches, evoke the rapidly changing moods of a blustery day. The sensitive observation of light-effects linking sky and ground is derived from Dutch seventeenth-century landscape painting, which the artist admired. The small group of a peasant girl with cattle in the right middle distance adds a pastoral touch, but this is subordinated to the painting's grand concept of nature.

M.A.R.

JEHUDO EPSTEIN

Austrian, 1870-1946

Born in Slonsk (Gouvernement Minsk, Russia), Epstein was to die in Johannesburg, South Africa. His father was a rabbi. At the age of eighteen, Epstein moved to Vienna where he studied at the Academy of Arts, soon playing an important part in the artistic life of that city. He travelled extensively (to Italy, Spain, France, Holland, Germany, and Palestine) and participated in many international exhibitions. His oeuvre consists of many genre scenes, often based on Jewish customs, and landscapes depicting motifs from countries he had visited; but above all he became an outstanding portrait painter. By 1920, he had received almost all of the important Austrian art prizes. Although it is not clear whether he ever became an Austrian citizen, he belongs to the sphere of Austrian painting.

Portrait of Frau Knoepfelmacher (79.194)

Signed and dated at lower right: *Jehudo Epstein III 1906.*
Canvas, *123.1 x 115.4 (48 x 45).*

Provenance
Kunsthandlung Karl Löscher/Anton Jancsy, Vienna.
Purchased for the Bass Collection 25 July 1966.

References
Bass Catalogue 1973, No. 194.

Exhibitions
Vienna, Herbstausstellung im Künstlerhaus Wien, 1906,
no. 259.
Venice, VII Esposizione Internationale d'Arte, 1907,
no. 751.

Epstein's painting remained unaffected by the fashionable stylistic trends at the turn of the century. The Bass painting happily combines the tradition of late-Baroque representational portraiture with a pre-expressionist freedom of form. The Munich painter Lovis Corinth seems to have served as an artistic inspiration. Nothing is known about the sitter.

G.F.

JEAN-BAPTISTE ARMAND GUILLAUMIN

French, 1841-1927

Born to the working class, Guillaumin studied briefly in Paris at the Académie Suisse. Here he met and formed close relationships with Pissarro and Cézanne, with whom he often painted. In 1874 Guillaumin joined Monet, Renoir, and Pissarro in founding the *Société anonyme des artistes peintres, sculpteurs, graveurs,* who were subsequently called the Impressionists. Guillaumin participated in all but two of the eight Impressionist exhibitions held between 1874 and 1886. In 1887 he became a friend of Van Gogh and responded to the new ideas which led the way to 'Post-Impressionism'. Towards the end of his life he adopted the intense colors and simplified forms used by the group of painters known as the Fauves.

Sand Hopper, Quai de Bercy (79.119)

Signed and dated at lower right: *Guillaumin, 12-87* [December 1887].
Pastel on paper, *64.1 x 97.4 (25 x 38).*

Provenance
Galérie Raphael Gerara, Paris, 1941.
Galérie Charpentier, Paris, 1944-1954.
Galéries Serret-Fauveau, Paris, 1964.

References
Christopher Gray, *Armand Guillaumin,* Chester, Ct. 1972, no. 104, pl. 15.
Bass Catalogue 1973, No. 119 (title: *The Seine at Paris).*

Exhibition
Paris, Exposition Guillaumin, 1907.

During the period 1885-1887, Guillaumin made many drawings and sketches of the Seine along the Quai de Bercy. The striking motif of a sand hopper features in some of these studies. The present pastel painting is the final version of the series. It dates from the year when the artist became a friend of Van Gogh, who is said to have been much interested in Guillaumin's pastel technique, which influenced his own handling of brushstrokes in painting (ref. Gray, p. 38).

Le Rocher de Génétin (79.122)

Signed at lower left: *Guillaumin.*
Painted c. 1895.
Canvas, *94.8 x 66.6 (37 x 26).*

Provenance
Collection Madame Leigeois (in collaboration with Galérie Blot).
Galéries Serret-Fauveau.

References
G. Serret and D. Fabiani, *Armand Guillaumin, 1841-1921, Catalogue raisonné de l'oeuvre peint,* Paris 1971, no. 330.
Bass Catalogue 1973, No. 122.

According to his own account, in 1893 Guillaumin discovered the picturesque village of Crozant, situated in the western foothills of the Massif Central at the confluence of the rivers Creuse and Sédelle. Crozant became his second home, where he lived and worked for several months every year painting the surrounding countryside in its varying moods. The rocky formations near Génétin on the river Creuse were a favorite motif. In the present painting, Guillaumin placed the solid mass of the rock in a dominant position on the right, building up its form in many geometric facets reminiscent of Cézanne's structured approach to nature. The landscape extending in the distance beyond the rock is observed in its vivid autumn colors, as suggested in the original title of the painting, *Last Days of October.*

GUILLAUMIN

Agay (79.118)

Signed at lower left: *Guillaumin*.
An inscription on the back, *Agay Mai 1901*, mentioned
in records, is no longer visible due to conservation
work.
Canvas, *66 x 92 (26 x 36½)*.

Provenance
Collection Raphaél Gérard, Paris.
Galéries Serret-Fauveau, Paris.

References
Gray, *Guillaumin*, no. 196, pl. 32.
Serret and Fabiani, *Catalogue raisonné*, no. 550.
Bass Catalogue 1973, No. 118.

Agay is a small town, situated on the Mediterranean coast
between Marseilles and Nice, where Guillaumin spent the
late winter and early spring year after year from 1892.
There he painted the rugged shapes of the rocks whose
vivid red color forms a striking contrast with the deep
Mediterranean blue of sea and sky and the clear green of the
pine trees. With his emphasis on strong clear colors and
simplified forms in paintings such as *Agay*, Guillaumin
anticipated the new trends later introduced by Matisse and
the Fauves.

Crozant, the Valley of the Sédelle (Pont Charraud) (79.123)

Signed at bottom right: *Guillaumin*.
Painted c. 1896-1897.
Canvas, *66.6 x 92.3 (26 x 36)*.

Provenance
Collection Durand-Ruel, Paris.
Galéries Serret-Fauveau, Paris, 1964.

References
Gray, *Guillaumin*, no. 177, pl. 142.
Serret and Fabiani, *Catalogue raisonné*, no. 373.
Bass Catalogue 1973, No. 123.

Exhibitions
Tampa, Florida, The Tampa Museum, *The Subjective Vision
of French Impressionism*, 1981, no. 34, illus. p. 38.

Pont Charraud was another frequent subject of
Guillaumin's paintings at Crozant. The composition of
this landscape with its undulating hills, rendered as a
sequence of contrasting color fields, suggests the influence
of Gauguin.

117

Crozant, Evening Scene (Les Grandes Gouttes) (79.121)

Signed at lower right: *Guillaumin.*
Date mentioned by Gray, "March 1902", no longer
visible.
Canvas, *61.5 x 74.3 (24 x 29).*

Provenance
Collection Blot, Paris.
Galéries Serret-Fauveau, Paris, 1964.

References
Gray, *Guillaumin,* no. 208, pl. 34.
Serret and Fabiani, *Catalogue raisonné,* no. 572.
Bass Catalogue 1973, No. 121.

Exhibitions
Tampa Museum, *Subjective Vision,* no. 35.

According to Gray, this painting was once inscribed
Crozant: Les Grandes Gouttes le soir. Mars 1902. The
inscription is no longer visible but the painting is
consistent with Guillaumin's style at the beginning of the
twentieth century. The rosy hues of an evening sky set the
key for the color nuances of this sensitive study of landscape.

La Creuse en Septembre (79.120)

Signed at lower left: *Guillaumin.*
Inscribed on back: *La Creuse en septembre 1903.*
Canvas, *61.5 x 74.3 (24 x 29).*

Provenance
Collection Blot, Paris.
Galéries Serret-Fauveau, Paris, 1964.

References
Gray, *Guillaumin,* no. 216, pl. 164.
Serret and Fabiani, *Catalogue raisonné,* no. 410.
Bass Catalogue 1973, No. 120.

Guillaumin frequently returned to Crozant in the fall to
paint the landscape in its autumn colors. This painting
should be compared with No. 79.122, *Le Rocher de
Génétin,* which is painted in a similar palette, although
the motif is quite different. The present composition does
not afford a view into the distance but focuses on three
large trees whose forms and patterns fill the first plane of
the picture. Guillaumin's emphasis on decorative pattern
again suggests the influence of Matisse.

M.A.R.

EUGEN (EUGÈNE) JETTEL

Austrian, 1845-1901

Born in Johnsdorf, Moravia (today CSSR), from 1860 Jettel studied with the landscape painter Albert Zimmermann at the Vienna Academy. Among his fellow students was the most important Austrian landscape painter of the late nineteenth century, Emil Jakob Schindler (1842-1892), with whom Jettel shared a new poetic vision of nature. From 1873 to 1895 Jettel lived in Paris, where he was impressed by the Barbizon painters. A contract with the Parisian art dealer Charles Sedelmayer, a native of Vienna, obliged Jettel to paint a great quantity of pictures.[1]

Canal near Reynsburg in Holland, at Dawn (79.196)

Signed and dated lower right: *Eugène Jettel 1893.*
Canvas, *63.4 x 88.5 (24¾ x 34½).*

Provenance
Kunsthandlung Anton Stöckl: Auction of the Sedelmayer Collection, Vienna, 27 February 1906, no. 47.
Kunsthandlung Karl Löscher/Anton Jancsy, Vienna.
Purchased 25 July 1966 for the Bass Collection.

References
Bass Catalogue 1973, No. 196.

Exhibitions
Annandale-on-Hudson, New York, Edith C. Blum Art Institute of Bard College (in cooperation with the De Pre Art Gallery of Hope College; IBM Gallery of Science and Art; Bass Museum of Art), *Pre-Modern Art of Vienna: 1848-1898,* 1987-1988.

Jettel made many trips from Paris to northern France and Holland. He preferred to paint flat landscapes, concentrating on the rendering of atmosphere and the varying effects of the sky. This painting emphasizes Jettel's predilection for nature in a quiet mood.

G.F.

1. H. Fuchs, *Eugen Jettel,* Vienna 1975.

MAXIMILIAN KURZWEIL

Austrian, 1867-1916

Born in Bisenz, Moravia (today CSSR), Kurzweil studied at the Vienna Academy from 1886. From 1892 to 1894 he worked in Paris where he joined the artists' colony of Concarneau. He married a woman from that city and from 1895 lived half a year in Vienna and half in southern France. In 1897 he was one of the co-founders of the *Secession,* the Viennese society of artists which gave the period around 1900 its special flavor. Its most important member was Gustav Klimt. Kurzweil undertook journeys to Italy and Dalmatia, but France was the decisive influence on his artistic development. In his early work he preferred subdued pastel shades, employing stronger hues only in his later career. He was a sensitive portraitist but mainly concentrated on landscape painting.

Still Life with Glasses (79.195)

Signed lower right: *Kurzweil.*
Painted between 1911-1916.
Canvas, *50 x 45.5 (19½ x 17¾).*

Provenance
Kunsthandlung Karl Löscher/Anton Jancsy, Vienna.
Purchased for the Bass Collection 25 July 1966.

References
F. Novotny and H. Adolph, *Max Kurzweil. Ein Maler der Wiener Secession,* Wien 1969, no. 203 *(Gläser auf Tasse).*
Bass Catalogue 1973, No. 195.

Exhibitions
Vienna, Oberes Belvedere, The Austrian Gallery,
November 1965 to March 1966.

This is one of Kurzweil's rare still-lifes. The work must have been the result of a momentary inspiration, when the artist attempted to capture the scintillating light reflections of the individual glasses. With its impressionist tendencies, the painting is exceptional for Vienna.

G.F.

HANS MAKART

Austrian, 1840-1884

Born in Salzburg, Hans Makart studied with the most famous German history painter of the period, Carl von Piloty, at the Munich Academy from 1860 to 1865. A few exhibitions in 1868 brought him instant fame and a summons from Kaiser Franz Joseph I to the imperial city of Vienna. The construction of the Ringstrasse was in full swing and a great number of artists were needed to decorate its monumental buildings.

Makart became the most influential history painter of his generation, introducing a new freedom of subject matter and an unusual richness of color which impressed his contemporaries. He led the life of a prince of painting, working in his sumptuous studio where he also gave his celebrated parties.

Makart had an influence not only on the painting of his time but also on fashion, interior decoration (the 'Makartbouquet' was to be found in almost every salon), and the theatre. Even now the years from 1870 to 1890 in Vienna are referred to as the 'Makart Period.'

The Valkyrie (79.188)

Signed lower right: *Hans Makart.*
Painted in 1877.
Panel, *129.5 x 85.25 (50½ x 33¼).*

Provenance

J.M. Heberle, Cologne, Auction 21-30 October 1895, No. 105 (described in the catalogue as "Portrait of the Baroness Teschenberg;" Pirchan [see ref.] and other scholars have corrected the identification of the sitter).
Kunsthandlung Karl Löscher/Anton Jancsy, Vienna.
Purchased for the Bass Collection 25 July 1966.

References

E. Ranzoni, *Hans Makarts Werke,* Vienna 1884, pl. 53.
Ann Tizia Leitich, *Verklungenes Wien,* Vienna 1942, ill. p. 103 (*Brunhilde*).
E. Pirchan, *Hans Makart. Leben, Werke und Zeit,* Vienna 1954, ill. 52, 53.
Gerbert Frodl, *Hans Makart. Monographie und Werkverzeichnis,* Salzburg 1974, no. 293, ill. p. 362.
Bass Catalogue 1973, No. 188.

Exhibitions

Vienna, Österreichischer Kunstverein, May/June 1877, no. 8; April 1878, no. 1.
Augsburg, Kunstverein, 1877.
Coral Gables, Florida, Lowe Art Museum, April 1979.
Annandale-on-Hudson, New York, Edith C. Blum Art Institute of Bard College (in cooperation with the Du Pre Art Gallery of Hope College; IBM Gallery of Science and Art; Bass Museum of Art), *Pre-Modern Art of Vienna: 1848-1898,* 1987-88.

Makart was known for his many virtuoso portraits of ladies. His sitters belonged to the aristocracy or to the theatre and he liked to portray them dressed up in historical, or fantasy, costume. This painting is a portrait of Helene von Racowitza dressed as a character from Wagner's *Ring der Nibelungen.* Makart was an ardent admirer of Richard Wagner (who was a guest in the artist's atelier on several occasions), and he painted a series of scenes from the *Ring* in Wagner's honor.

The sitter of *The Valkyrie* was an actress and celebrated beauty, with the notoriety of a *femme fatale:* when she was a young girl in 1864 her fiancé fought a duel on her behalf in which the famous German political theorist and founder of the German workers' movement, Ferdinand Lasalle, was killed. Makart was fascinated with Helene's Titianesque red-gold hair, a color he most admired, and he had been hoping to paint her for years before achieving his ambition. The painting of *The Valkyrie* was acclaimed as a masterpiece and included in several important exhibitions. It is a prime example of a historicizing portrait, reverting to a sixteenth-century tradition well represented in the works of Titian.

G.F.

EMANUEL NOTTERMAN,

Belgian, 1808-1863

Emanuel Notterman was a pupil of Baptist Loderwyck Maes (Maes-Canini) and Petrus Cremer. He worked in Antwerp as a painter of portraits and genre scenes. The artist seems to have made a specialty of 'humorous' animal subjects. A pair of small oil paintings on panel featuring a dog as painter and a dogs' musical trio was sold at Sotheby's 9 May 1979 (lot 50). Another larger painting of monkeys washing dishes was sold at Sotheby's 20 June 1977 (lot 81).

Monkeys' Concert Party (79.322)

Signed and dated lower right: *E. Notterman 1877.*
Panel, *44.8 x 35.9 (17½ x 14).*

Provenance
Purchased from Sotheby's Parke-Bernet, 21 April 1971, lot 254.

References
Bass Catalogue 1973, No. 322.

The Bass painting is described in the Sotheby's Parke-Bernet catalogue as "An interior with a monkey vigorously playing a clarinet, while a companion playing a cello urges him on."

Some seventeenth-century Antwerp painters, such as David Teniers II (1610-1690) occasionally depicted simian subjects. It is possible that Notterman followed their example.

M.A.R.

Conditions: The picture is dark and in need of cleaning.

ADOLF PICHLER

Hungarian, 1835-1905

Adolf Pichler was born in Cziffer, Hungary, but spent most of his adult life in Munich, where he studied with the animal painter Friedrich Voltz. In his time he was a well-known painter, closely connected with the Munich art scene, who found his place in monographs of Munich art, for instance F. Pecht's *Geschichte der Münchner Kunst* (1888).

Portrait of a Rabbi (79.202)

Inscribed in pencil on cardboard backing of painting:
. . . [illegible line].
Original Skizze
Historienmaler
Adolf Pichler München
Attached above the inscription is a photograph of the rabbi who served as a model for the portrait. A seal in the upper right corner of the backing is no longer readable.

Panel, *46.2 x 35.9 (14 x 11).*

Provenance
Kunsthandlung Karl Löscher/Anton Jancsy, Vienna.
Purchased for the Bass Collection 25 July 1966.

References
Bass Catalogue 1973, No. 202.

Representations of Jewish subjects, such as portraits and genre scenes, were popular in Munich in the late nineteenth century and around 1900. This is probably a study for a larger picture, possibly with several figures.

G.F.

EDMUND PICK-MORINO

Austrian, 1877-1958

Oedon Pick, who changed his name to Edmund Pick-Morino around 1900, was born in Komorn, Hungary (today Komarno, CSSR). He came to Vienna as a child and in 1898 went to study at the Munich Academy, but he was mainly influenced by expressionist painters outside the Academy, such as Lovis Corinth. From 1910 he lived again in Vienna and in 1921 he became a member of the Vienna Künstlerhaus where he regularly exhibited. In 1929 the artist settled in France and undertook journeys to Italy, Germany, Hungary, and the Near Orient. From 1939 he lived in Hungary and left only briefly before his death, which occurred in Dielbeck near Brussels, Belgium. Pick-Morino's favorite themes were city views, portraits, and small-scale still-lifes with few objects.

Head of a Lady Dressed in Red (79.215)

Painted c. 1925.
Canvas, 34.6 x 31.7 (13½ x 12⅜).

Provenance
Kunsthandlung Karl Löscher/Anton Jancsy, Vienna.
Purchased for the Bass Collection 25 July 1966

References
H. Hutter, *Edmund Pick-Morino*, Vienna 1959, no. 163.
Bass Catalogue 1973, No. 215.

The picture is characteristic of the artist's style after 1920 when he abandoned the delicate tonality of French painting and adopted a broader, more vigorous technique and looser brushwork. In this way he responded to the dominant trend of his new artistic environment, namely Austrian expressionism in its Viennese variant.

The Painter Oskar Laske at His Easel (79.209)

Inscribed and signed lower right, *Oskar Laske als Kriegsmaler/Pick Morino.*
Painted before 1918.
Canvas, 80.2 x 64.7 (31¼ x 25¼)

Provenance
Kunsthandlung Karl Löscher/Anton Jancsy, Vienna.
Purchased for the Bass Collection 25 July 1966.

References
Hutter, *Pick-Morino*, no. 169.
Bass Catalogue 1973, No. 209.

Oskar Laske was a well-known Viennese painter whose work did not reflect any of the contemporary stylistic norms (i.e. it was neither expressionist nor in the Jugendstil). His paintings expressed a critical, even sarcastic attitude to his era. He frequently worked as an illustrator. Pick-Morino protrays him absorbed in his work and full of confidence.

G.F.

EMIL RAU

German, 1858-1919

Born in Dresden, Emil Rau received his first artistic training at the Dresden Academy. In 1879 he went to study at the Munich Academy, which at that time held a great attraction for young artists of German-speaking countries. His studies terminated in 1883. He favored above all themes from the peasant milieu of Upper Bavaria, which had the same popular appeal as the Tyrolean peasant scenes painted by the contemporary Munich artist Franz Defregger.

Afternoon on the Terrace (79.284)

Signed lower left: *E. RAU.*
Canvas, *121.8 x 153.8 (47½ x 60).*
A label on the middle bottom stretcher bears the inscription: *Emil Plesko München Baier Str 82. Geschäft Für Einrahmungen, Vergold Imitation.*

Provenance
Galerie Wimmer & Co., Munich.
Purchased for the Bass Museum 14 August 1969.

References
Bass Catalogue 1973, No. 284.

The rural genre scene takes place outside a farm probably situated in the Ramsau valley. This idyllic region near Berchtesgaden was particularly popular with German and Austrian painters of the nineteenth century who appreciated its unspoiled charm. Rau was not greatly interested in landscape but attempted to convey the peace and contentment of rural life. The painting is typical of the nineteenth-century city dweller's romantic interpretation of country life.

The Greeting ("Grüss Gott") (79.285)

Signed lower right: *E. RAU.*
Canvas, *101.6 x 82 (40 x 32¼)*
Inscribed label on back: *Gewis...Beratung Nr. 10262 Künstler: Rau. Titel: "Grüss Gott."*

Provenance
Galerie Wimmer & Co., Munich.
Purchased for the Bass Collection 14 August 1969.

References
Bass Catalogue 1973, No. 285.

This little episode probably also takes place in the Ramsau near Berchtesgaden.

G.F.

JOHANN BAPTIST REITER

Austrian, 1813-1890

Johann Reiter first worked with his father, who was a cabinet-maker in Linz (Upper Austria), but in 1830 he became a student at the Vienna Academy. In 1835 he painted altarpieces for a church in Upper Austria, and in the following years he developed into a respectable painter of portraits and genre scenes. His paintings were regularly seen in Viennese exhibitions. He was one of the few Austrian painters of his period who treated the subject of simple workers. His late work (after 1860) was somewhat superficial, but before that he created many unusually realistic paintings which are distinguished by their compositional originality.

Portrait of a Lady (79.187)

Painted c. 1845-1850.
Canvas, *68.5 x 53.2 (26¾ x 20¾).*

Provenance
Galerie Am Michaelerplatz [Melitta Fischer], Vienna.
Purchased for the Bass Collection 27 July 1966.

References
Bass Catalogue 1973, No. 187 (as Viennese master, about 1820).

This portrait is unusual for its period because ladies were not normally portrayed with bare shoulders, but dressed in correct formal garments. The picture shows every sign of being painted by Reiter. He frequently ignored rigid traditions and created pictures with a personal approach to composition and mood. This portrait is distinguished by its intimate mood and great individuality. These qualities, as well as the animated smile of the girl and the relatively free brushwork, testify to Reiter's authorship.

G.F.

FRANZ SCHROTZBERG

Austrian, 1811-1889

Born in Vienna, Franz Schrotzberg studied at the Vienna Academy from 1825 and soon became one of the most famous portrait painters of his native city. His patrons were mostly aristocrats and personages from the circle of the imperial court. Schrotzberg travelled to Germany, Italy, Paris, and London. In his later career the critics somewhat disparagingly referred to him as a 'fashion painter.' He never was a realist and always emphasized the attractive and positive features of his sitters. This tendency to idealize greatly contributed to his success.

Kaiserin Elisabeth of Austria (63.40)

Painted 1856.
Canvas, *85 x 68 (33 x 26¾).*

Provenance
Bass Collection, 1963.

References
Von Wurzbach, *Biographisches Lexikon,* vol. 32, under Schrotzberg.
Bass Catalogue 1973, No. 40.

Elisabeth (1837-1898), much admired for her beauty, was the daughter of Duke Joseph of Bavaria. Contemporaries and posterity affectionately abbreviated her name to 'Sissy.' Her marriage to Franz Joseph, which took place in 1854, was not harmonious, and behind the glitter of the imperial court her life was not a happy one. The suicide of her only son, Crown Prince Rudolf, at Meyerling in 1889, was a tragedy from which she never recovered. She embarked on a life of restless travelling and was assassinated by an anarchist in Geneva in 1898.

Kaiser Franz Joseph I of Austria (63.39)

Painted 1856.
Canvas, *85 x 68 (33 x 26¾).*
Inscribed on verso: *W. Koller and C. Wien Silber Medaille.*

Provenance
Bass Collection, 1963.

References
C.v. Wurzbach, *Biographisches Lexikon des Kaiserthums Österreich,* vol. 32, Vienna 1876, under the entry for Schrotzberg.
Bass Catalogue 1973, No. 39.

Kaiser Franz Joseph I, born 1830, was Emperor of Austria from 1848 (the year of the revolution) to his death in 1916. This is an official portrait showing the young emperor in his gala uniform with all his medals.

During Franz Joseph's long reign, Austria experienced a 'golden age.' The arts flourished and magnificent new buildings, springing up all over Vienna and particularly along the Ringstrasse, gave the city its present-day architectural grandeur.

G.F.

FERDINAND STRANSKY

Austrian, 1904-1981

Born in Lower Austria, Ferdinand Stransky was trained as a restorer in the Vienna Academy from 1919 to 1923, and throughout his life he successfully practiced this profession, at the same time pursuing a career as a painter. Stransky became a member of various Viennese artists' societies, among them the Secession. He was the recipient of several prizes, such as the Grand Austrian State Prize. His work forms a bridge from the Viennese Expressionism of the 1930s to the neo-expressionism of the years following the Second World War. He belongs to the generation of Austrian artists whose careers were interrupted by the war, but unlike many others he succeeded in reestablishing his career as a painter.

Theresianumgasse II (79.190)

Signed lower left: *F. Stransky.*
Painted 1959.
Canvas, *90.25 x 101.3 (35⅛ x 39½).*

Provenance
Kunsthandlung Karl Löscher/Anton Jancsy, Vienna.
Purchased for the Bass Collection 25 July 1966.

References
Moderne Kunst in Österreich, Vienna 1965,
p. 56.
Bass Catalogue 1973, No. 190.

The picture shows a view from the painter's studio in Vienna. The artist was not primarily aiming at topographical exactitude but wished to capture the precise conditions created by the season, the weather, the time of day. The familiar view from his window became an emotional experience. Stransky had painted the same view a year earlier (*Theresianumgasse I*).

G.F.

HEINRICH TOMEC

Austrian, 1863-1928

Heinrich Tomec was born in Prague and received his first training from 1879 to 1884 in the painting workshop of the Czech National Theatre. From 1887 to 1892 he studied at the Vienna Academy. In 1896 he became a member of the Künstlerhaus, and in 1900 of the Hagenbund, a more progressive artists' association. He spent the rest of his life in Vienna. Tomec's oeuvre consists largely of landscapes painted in bright sunny hues, for which the artist received a great number of prizes and medals, among them the 'Emperor's Prize' in 1910.

Church Interior (79.192)

Signed and dated lower right: *Tomec 1924.*
Canvas, *117.9 x 95.8 (46 x 37⅜).*

Provenance
Kunsthandlung Karl Löscher/Anton Jancsy, Vienna.
Purchased for the Bass Collection 25 July 1966.

References
Bass Catalogue 1973, No. 192.

Tomec has painted the interior of a typical Austrian or Bohemian Baroque church and has enlivened the space with a congregation listening attentively to the sermon. The painter was less concerned with precise details of the architecture than with evoking a mood, an atmosphere. Tomec's interest in Baroque architecture began shortly after 1900; however he never forgot to include the human element in his paintings of church interiors.

G.F.

EDUARD VEITH

Austrian, 1856-1925

Born in Neutitschein (today Novy Jicin, CSSR), Eduard Veith lived and died in Vienna. He attended the Vienna Kunstgewerbeschule, an arts and crafts college, from 1873 to 1877. In those years Hans Makart was at the height of his career and Veith was understandably impressed with the work of Vienna's most famous painter. Like Makart he became a much-sought-after and productive painter of monumental pictures. He created decorations for several large theatres in Prague and Vienna and large-scale historical scenes for the Hofburg (the Emperor's residence) in Vienna. From 1890 Veith was a member of the Künstlerhaus, where he exhibited over many years. Apart from historical and allegorical subjects he produced many landscapes and portraits.

The Holy Family (Rest on the Flight into Egypt) (79.193)

Signed and dated lower right: *E. VEITH/VIENNA 1902.*
Canvas, *76.9 x 112.8 (30 x 44).*
Label on back with printed text, *Grosse-Berliner-Kunst-Ausstellung 1904,* and crayon inscription *E. Veith.*

Provenance
Kunsthandlung Karl Löscher/Anton Jancsy, Vienna.
Purchased for the Bass Collection 25 July 1966.

References
Bass Catalogue 1973, No. 193.

Exhibitions
Vienna, Wiener Künstlerhaus, 1902.
Berlin, Grosse Berliner Kunstausstellung, 1904.
Vienna, Wiener Künstlerhaus, Gedächtnisausstellung, 1925, no. 253.
Inscribed on stretcher *Reproduktions Recht 300 Berlin.*

Veith was a very versatile artist in both subject and technique, however he rarely painted religious subjects. Towards the end of the century he abandoned his neo-Baroque manner, influenced by Makart, in favor of an almost Renaissance serenity. The *Holy Family* is a beautiful example of this new phase in Veith's style, which remained unaffected by the Jugendstil, then at its first peak. Veith's paintings are distinguished by their coloristic refinement and their careful finish in every detail. For the *Holy Family* he received the 'Great Gold Medal.'

G.F.

ECCLESIASTICAL NEEDLEWORK

Glossary of Technical Terminology Relating to Textiles

Antependium: altar frontal; a decorative covering for the front of the altar.

Apparel: nearly-square panel used as decoration on the front and back of the skirt of the dalmatic.

Burse: purse-like container for the corporal, the linen upon which the host and chalice are placed during the Mass. Composed of two pieces of stiffened paper or cardboard covered on the outside with fabric matching the other vestments, the burse may be sewn closed on three sides, with two vents, or stitched on one side and tied shut with ribbons.

Dalmatic: tunic-shaped vestment worn by deacon and sub-deacon.

Fanons: the two lappets attached to the base of the back of the mitre and falling over the shoulders of the wearer.

Filé: composite yarn, smooth in appearance, consisting of a lamella (flat strip of gilt precious or base metal, membrane, paper, or leather) wound about a core thread.

Frisé: composite yarn, undulating in appearance, consisting of a lamella wound about a two-ply core thread of which each element has a different degree of twist.

Galloon: narrow, woven decorative band, usually of silk and metal thread.

Gremial: rectangular or square piece of fabric, usually matching the other vestments, that is placed over the bishop's lap when seated during High Mass and also during ordinations when he is anointing with oils; no longer used.

Laid and couched work: needlework in which first one set of threads is stitched, or laid down. These threads are secured (couched) by others worked perpendicular to the first.

Maniple: long, narrow vestment, usually of the same material as the stole and chasuble, formerly worn over the left forearm but now no longer used.

Morse: decorative clasp used to fasten the front of the cope.

Ornat: German term used to designate the complete set of vestments worn for a solemn High Mass.

Or nué: literally, shaded gold. A type of embroidery in which metal threads (filé) are laid down and secured by silk threads, which may in areas totally cover the metal, to produce a very painterly effect.

Orphreys: woven or embroidered decorative bands applied to cope or chasuble.

SPAIN (probably Toledo)

Second quarter of the sixteenth century

Altar Frontal (79.426)

Silk and metal thread embroidery on silk velvet,
123.5 x 253.2 (48⅝ x 99⅝) including frame.
Twentieth-century Renaissance style wooden frame.

Provenance
Possibly from the church of San Juan de los Reyes, Toledo.
Purchased by French and Co. from Spanish Art Galleries,
London, 19 November 1914.
R.B. Mellon, Pittsburgh, 1924.
Sarah Mellon Scaife, Pittsburgh.
Purchased for the Bass Collection from Milton Samuels,
1971.

References
Christa Mayer Thurman, *Raiment for the Lord's Service,* exh.
cat., Art Institute of Chicago, Chicago 1975, p. 168
(mentions this piece as the Pittsburgh altar frontal and
discusses its relationship to examples in Chicago, London,
and San Franciso).
Bass Catalogue 1973, No. 426 (as Italian, c. 1600).

The altar frontal consists of four separate areas, each of
which has a ground fabric of pieced dark-red velvet in
weak condition. The three large figural medallions in the
center, and the seven smaller ones, five in the superfrontal
and one in each side border, are executed in *or nué*
embroidery; faces and hands are worked in silk in split
stitch and the raised outlines are achieved by couching
down cords of silk and metal thread. The roundels and
the secondary motifs are primarily in laid and couched
embroidery using gilt metal thread bound by silk,
sometimes worked over linen for additional height. Some
leaves are worked in *or nué;* details are rendered in silk
by split stitch. A woven silk and metal thread galloon is
attached to the inner borders, with the fourth, that at the
bottom, being a galloon of a different design than the
others. The embroidery is of very high quality, although
worn and with later restorations. The antependium has
been mounted on a stretcher and put into a later wooden
frame.

The altar frontal possibly comes from the church of
San Juan de los Reyes in Toledo. While this has not been
confirmed, the predominance of iconographical references
to and depictions of Saint John—the Divine, the
Evangelist, the Beloved Disciple, the Apostle, all thought
until this century to be the same person—gives further
credence to this provenance. The center area contains three
large pictorial medallions each encircled by a wreath tied
with ribbons. The first two scenes depict legends
associated with Saint John the Divine. At left is the
assumption of the saint into heaven, with the four doctors

of the Church—Jerome, Augustine, Ambrose, and
Gregory the Great—below. A scene from the apocryphal
story of John's visit to Rome at the command of the
Emperor Domitian is illustrated in the second medallion:
the attempted martyrdom of the saint by boiling him in
oil when he refused to acknowledge the divinity of the
emperor. John is shown protected by heavenly rays and
standing in the cauldron while three figures in antique-
style dress feed the flames, stoke the fire, and stir the
liquid. In the medallion at right is John the Evangelist
accompanied by three angels and an eagle, his attribute.
This nimbed eagle appears again throughout the altar
frontal, prominently to either side of the central
medallion, and as part of the secondary decoration in
the superfrontal and side borders.

References to John continue in the left, center, and
right medallions in the superfrontal. The basis of the
illustration at left is another apocryphal story. At Ephesus
Saint John was challenged by the high priest of Diana
to drink from a poisoned cup in order to prove the
superiority of his God. John made the sign of the cross
over the cup, the poison emerged in the shape of a serpent,
and the saint safely drank the contents. At far right the
aged saint with long beard and tablets may well be a
reference to the longevity of John and the Apocalypse
which he wrote while exiled on the island of Patmos. In
the central medallion is the Crucifixion with the Virgin
Mary, Mary Magdalen, and Saint John. This is an
appropriate placement for the scene as it stresses John's
role as the beloved disciple, the only apostle present at the
Crucifixion and the one to whom Christ entrusted the care
of his mother.

In the adjacent medallions Saints Peter and Paul are
depicted, while in the side borders are shown Saint Agnes,
at left, and Saint Apollonia at right. The interstitial motifs
are variants·of floral and foliage arabesques and scrolls,
some emanating from or flanking urns. The edges of the
superfrontal and the side panels are bordered by a scrolling
leaf pattern, while the bottom border of the central area is
decorated with alternating stylized flowers and leaves.

The altar frontal is closely related to another, also with
a provenance to San Juan de los Reyes and now in the
Victoria and Albert Museum, London.[1] Although the two
center medallions in this piece illustrate scenes from the
life of Saint John the Baptist—the Baptism of Christ, and
the Virgin and Child with Saint John—two of the
roundels in the superfrontal repeat major scenes from the
Bass embroidery: the attempted martyrdom of Saint John
and the Evangelist accompanied by angels. The eagle,

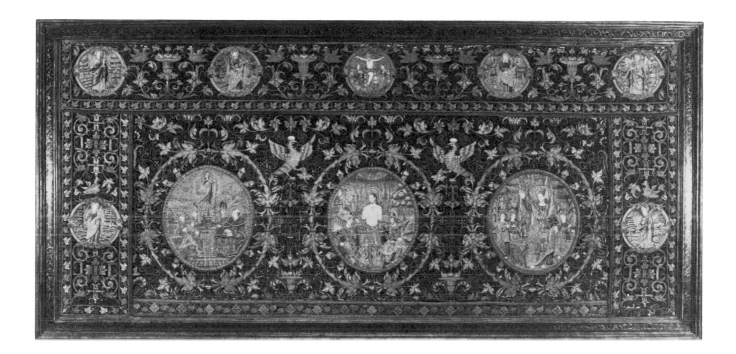

which figures so prominently in the Bass altar frontal, is emphasized in the London example by placing the symbol in a roundel to either side of the central scene, which, as in the Bass piece, is an event from the Passion of Christ, here the carrying of the cross. The floriated frames surrounding the small medallions are nearly identical in the two pieces, and the interstitial decoration of the superfrontal is very similar.

Other stylistic parallels can be found with altar frontals in the Art Institute of Chicago, the M.H. de Young Museum in San Francisco, and the Metropolitan Museum of Art, New York.[2] All but the last-mentioned piece have a similar history, having been purchased at auction in 1914 by French and Co. from the Spanish Art Galleries in London.[3] Further examination of the interrelationship of the Bass and Victoria and Albert altar frontals, as well as the group as a whole, is in order.

A.M.Z.

1. Donald King, "Medieval and Renaissance Embroidery from Spain," *Victoria and Albert Yearbook* 2, 1970, ill. p. 55; p. 59ff.
2. Helen Candee Churchill, "Four Spanish Embroideries of the Sixteenth Century," *Arts and Decoration,* 5, 1915, p. 271 and frontis. (ill. Chicago piece). The Chicago example, acc. no. 1944.623, is illustrated and discussed by Christa Mayer Thurman (see ref.), p. 166f. San Francisco, acc. no. 707.27; Metropolitan Museum of Art, acc. no. 07.287.2.
3. French and Co. files.

ITALY

First quarter of the seventeenth century

Chasuble with embroidered orphreys depicting the Virgin Mary and Franciscan saints (79.140)

Chasuble, silk velvet; orphreys, silk and metal thread embroidery and painted silk appliqué on silk velvet, *118 (shoulder to hem) x 77 (46½ x 30¼)*.

References
Bass Catalogue 1973, No. 140 (as Italian, fifteenth century).

The chasuble has been reassembled, the brick-red velvet being of later date than the orphreys. The figures of the saints and the Virgin are embroidered with polychrome silks (blue, gold, beige, and red) in split and outline stitch and with gilt metal thread, filé and purl, in laid and couched work. Faces and hands as well as the interstitial pattern of vases and flowers and the cartouches framing the saints are of applied silk, painted and embroidered, with the more architectural elements outlined with silk cord. Aureoles surrounding the figures are of purl, both smooth and faceted.

The background of the orphrey band is a red silk velvet for all but the figure of the Virgin, who is seen against a silk lamé ground. Three different woven galloons of silk and metal thread are used to border the orphrey bands, bind the neck and the outside edge of the chasuble. The vestment is lined with pale pink plain weave glazed linen. The overall condition is good although the figures, especially those on the front, are worn.

The iconography of the embroideries is very interesting and specific as all four saints are Franciscans, an order of friars founded by St. Francis of Assisi between 1207 and 1208 and legally established by Pope Innocent III in 1210. The guiding principles were absolute poverty, chastity, and obedience combined with a rigorous spiritual life, although subsequent factions allowed for personal and communal property.

On the back of the chasuble the Virgin is depicted at the top on a crescent moon above a seraph and surrounded by a cloud mandorla. Although no serpent is shown, this is probably the Virgin under her title of the Immaculate Conception, a dogma promulgated by the Franciscans long before it was officially declared in 1854. Directly below is Saint Francis of Assisi (1181-1226), exhibiting the stigmata and carrying a cross, symbol of his devotion to prayer. Saint Anthony of Padua (1195-1231), a friend of Saint Francis and a renowned preacher, is depicted with his attributes: a Bible to denote his scholarship and that he was a Doctor of the Church; a lily to symbolize his purity; and the Christ Child, who appeared to the saint.

On the front of the chasuble, wearing his cardinal's robes and hat, is Saint Bonaventura (1221-1274), great scholar and theologian, Minister General of the Franciscan Order and secretary to Pope Gregory X. Saint Paschal Baylon is shown in Franciscan habit with a book and the host to denote his special devotion to the Blessed Sacrament. As Paschal died in 1592 and was beatified in 1618, the orphrey must date from the first quarter of the seventeenth century although stylistically it continues the tradition of the late sixteenth century.

Great care was taken to individualize the features of the saints. The grouping of four major Franciscans, including the Spanish-born Paschal who belonged to the strict Observant Friars Minor, a group who sought to reestablish the primitive rule as begun by St. Francis, implies the continuity of the order as founded and indicates that the orphreys were intended as decorations for a vestment to be used by a Franciscan Community.

A.M.Z.

A: Front

B: Back

153

AUSTRIA (Vienna)

Late seventeenth-early eighteenth century

Bishop's Mitre (79.317.1)

Silk and metal thread embroidery on silk; purl, paillettes, metal studs, colored glass, paper interlining, 89.5 (*including fanons*) x 35 (35¼ x 13¾).

Provenance
Renato Bacchi, Milan, before 1968.
Acquired for the Bass Collection from the Blumka Gallery, New York, 1971.

References
Bass Catalogue 1973, No. 317.

The ground fabric of the mitre is a plain weave ribbed yellow silk embroidered both front and back with a symmetrical stylized floral pattern in polychrome silks and a variety of metal threads, filé and frisé. The embroidery is exceptionally textural. White, yellow, light and dark orange, light blue, green, and violet silks are used to render the floral elements and some of the leaves by a stitch that produces a loop and whose effect resembles uncut velvet. These forms are outlined with gold and silver frisé threads which, together with filé threads, are also used in laid and couched work to achieve the underlying compositional elements and branches and leaves. The gold filé is secured in diamond and diaper patterns by blue and pink silk, the silver by pink and green; the silver filé is couched in a 3/3 brick pattern with white silk. For raised work the gold filé is worked over paper and edged with a silk and metal cord.

The cross on the front of the mitre is worked with metal studs and purl; on the back the same materials are used to frame red glass at the heart of a stylized pomegranate. The mitre and fanons are edged with a narrow gold galloon woven in silk and metal thread. Beneath the blue silk lining can be seen a contemporary music manuscript used as an interlining. The two halves of the mitre are attached only at the sides.

The overall richness of the surface of the mitre is achieved through the extremely varied textural quality of the embroidery as well as the combination of materials and is representative of Austrian needlework of excellence of this period and later.[1] Characteristic of this type of metal thread embroidery is the contrast of various kinds of gold and silver threads worked in different levels of relief, couched in a variety of patterns by polychrome silks and combined with purl, paillettes, studs, and stones.[2] Also typical is the symmetrical and stylized pattern. The alternative contemporary trend in embroidery, naturalistic flowers rendered with polychrome silks (cf. *Rosenornat* entry) has only slight influence here as seen in the shading of the floral elements.

1. As can be seen by a comparison of this mitre with another, made in Vienna c. 1760, now in the treasury of Zagreb Cathedral; see Zdenka Munk, *Riznica zagrebacke katedrale,* exh. cat., Muzejski prostor, Zagreb 1983, ill. 78 and 113.
2. Dora Heinz, *Meisterwerke barocker Textilkunst,* exh. cat. Schloss Gobelsburg and Österreichisches Museum fur angewandte Kunst, Vienna 1972, p. 8ff.

A.M.Z.

A: Front

B: Back

155

AUSTRIA (Vienna)

Late seventeenth-early eighteenth century

Nineteen pieces from a set of vestments called the *Rosenornat,* dated c. 1700. Silk and metal embroidery on silk lamé and linen.

Cope (63.58.1), *151.1 (including morse) x 305.7 (59½ x 120¼).*

Chasuble (63.58.2), *109.2 x 73 (43 x 28¾).*

Chasuble (63.58.3), *110.5 x 73.7 (43½ x 29).*

Dalmatic (63.58.4), *105 x 105.3 (41¼ x 41½) shoulder to hem and cuff to cuff.*

Stole (63.58.5), *231.7 x 22 (91¼ x 8⅝).*

Stole (63.58.6), *231.2 x 21 (91 x 8¼).*

Stole (63.58.7), *230.5 x 21 (90¾ x 8¼).*

Maniple (63.58.8), *83.5 x 19.6 (32⅞ x 7¾).*

Maniple (63.58.9), *83 x 21.5 (32⅝ x 8½).*

Maniple (63.58.10), *84 x 22.8 (33 x 9).*

Gremial (63.58.11), *81.5 x 72.5 (32⅛ x 28⅛).*

Chalice Veil (63.58.12), *61 x 61 (24 x 24) including lace.*

Chalice Veil (63.58.13), *59.7 x 62.2 (23½ x 24½).*

Burse (63.58.14), *23.8 x 25 (9⅜ x 9⅞).*

Burse (63.58.15), *25 x 23.8 (9⅞ x 9⅜).*

Altar Frontal (63.58.16), *81.3 x 310.1 (32 x 122).*

Dalmatic (63.58.17), *104 x 106 (41 x 41¾) shoulder to hem and cuff to cuff.*

Altar Frontal (63.58.18), *75.5 x 230.5 (29¾ x 90¾).*

Altar Frontal (63.58.19), *61.6 x 231.5 (24¼ x 91¼).*

Provenance

The Ursuline Convent, Vienna (made by the sisters).
Bought from ProArte, Salzburg, for the Bass Collection.

References

Dora Heinz, *Meisterwerke barocker Textilkunst,* exh. cat., Schloss Gobelsburg and Österreichisches Museum für angewandte Kunst, Vienna 1972, pp. 31-32 (information from the Archive of the Ursulinenkloster Wein-Mauer). Bass Catalogue 1973, No. 58.
Harriet Bridgeman and Elizabeth Drury, eds., *Needlework,* New York 1978, p. 208 (mentions thirty pieces).

The ground fabric of the vestments is of two types: plain weave linen (63.58.1 [shield and orphrey], .3, .11, .12, .17-.19) and a plain weave ribbed white lamé silk. For the first group the background is worked with silver filé thread laid and couched with white silk in a twill pattern. The embroidered decoration of the vestments is the same throughout: polychrome silks in satin, stem and split stitches, laid and couched work and French knots; gold and silver filé thread is laid and couched. Some of the vestments have a modern red cotton satin lining (.4, .6-.9, .12), others an older salmon pink plain weave silk; the cope is lined with salmon pink cotton.

Nearly all the vestments have a mark, *VR. WIEN I.,* embroidered in stem stitch in yellow silk on the lining, old or new (on .12 it has been cut out, and there is no mark on .1, .14, .16, .18, .19). Narrow silk and metal woven galloons are used to bind the edges of the vestments and wider ones are used for additional decorations (no galloons on .11, .13, .16, .18, .19).

The cope closes with a contemporary Austrian or German gilt metal morse which depicts the Sacred Heart. There is no embroidery beneath the shield which attaches to the cope with three silk and metal buttons. One stole (.7) has a white linen cloth at the neck. The gremial is edged with wide metal lace and both chalice veils with narrower lace. The two burses are interlined with pages from a printed manuscript. All of the altar frontals are dubious as such although made from the original embroidery. They are pieced and lined with coarse bast fabric; two have a gold metal bobbin lace border with an ecclesiastical pattern of wheat and grapes. The condition of the vestments ranges from excellent to worn.

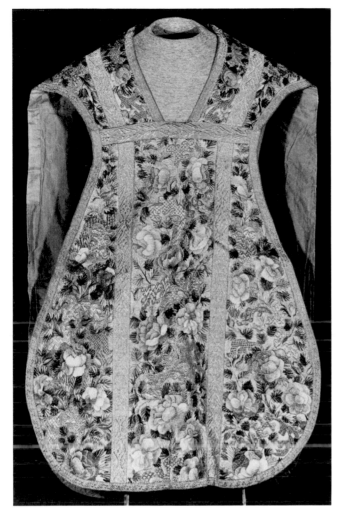

Chasuble (63.58.2)   A: Front   B: Back

AUSTRIA (VIENNA)

The sisters of the Ursuline convent in Johannesgasse are said to have begun the embroidery of the *Rosenornat* vestments in 1683 during the siege of Vienna by the Turks and to have finished the pontifical set in the first decade of the eighteenth century (ref. Dora Heinz). Considering the numerous pieces to the set it is not impossible that the work could have taken twenty years (ref. Bridgeman and Drury). Although made by nuns for use in the convent, the embroidery is of exceptionally high quality, which is not surprising as during this period there is often little difference in excellence between the work of professional embroiderers and that of talented and devoted amateurs, religious or lay.[1]

The pattern of the vestments—a profusion of roses, buds to full-blown blossoms, often arranged symmetrically—and its meticulous execution in shades ranging from white to rose to russet to red, the tonalities varying with the vestments, make this an excellent example of the naturalistic designs in Austrian needlework which developed in the last quarter of the seventeenth century under the influence of contemporary sample books, miniature painting, and Dutch floral paintings.[2] Sometimes the blossoms are shown individually, sometimes grouped and tied with blue bows (as on the gremial and chalice veils). The leaves and stems are rendered with equal care for shading nuances. The metallic sheen of the larger stylized leaves and branches and the silver of the ground, embroidered or woven, are in contrast to this naturalism.

Four other vestments from this set—a cope, a chasuble, a dalmatic and a maniple—are in the Österreichisches Museum für angewandte Kunst in Vienna.[3]

A.M.Z.

1. Dora Heinz, *Meisterwerke barocker Textilkunst,* exh. cat. Schloss Gobelsburg and Österreichisches Museum für angewandte Kunst, Vienna 1972, p. 10.
2. *Ibid.,* pp. 10-11.
3. For descriptions, discussions, and illustrations see Heinz, *Meisterwerke,* pp. 31-32, no. 13, colorpl. IV opp. p. 17; Christa C. Mayer Thurman, *Raiment for the Lord's Service,* exh. cat., Art Institute of Chicago, Chicago 1975, pp. 218-19, no. 103; Harriet Bridgeman and Elizabeth Drury, eds., *Needlework,* New York 1978, pp. 207 (ill. in color), 208, and 224.

1). Gremial (63.58.11)

2). Chalice Veil (63.58.12)

159

AUSTRIA (Vienna)

1773

Six vestments from the *Maria Theresia Ornat,* dated 1773. Silk and metal thread embroidery on silk, purl, paillettes.

Cope (63.59.1), *142 x 293.3 (55⅞ x 115½).*

Chalice Veil (63.59.2), *60.3 x 61 (23¾ x 24) including lace which is 4.3 (1¾) deep.*

Dalmatic (63.59.3), *105.7 x 121.3 (41⅝ x 47¾) shoulder to hem and cuff to cuff.*

Dalmatic (63.59.4), *104 x 122 (41 x 48) shoulder to hem and cuff to cuff.*

Stole (63.59.5), *210.8 x 22.2 (83 x 8¾).*

Maniple (63.59.6), *90.2 x 22.2 (35½ x 8¾).*

Provenance

Probably made for a convent for titled ladies in Prague.

References

Bass Catalogue 1973, No. 59.

All the vestments are made of a white silk ribbed plain weave moiré. The floral patterns, which are nearly symmetrical on the cope, dalmatics, and chalice veil, are achieved by using applied silk ombré ribbons. The edges of the forms, under which paper can sometimes be detected, are over-embroidered with silk thread of complementary color in satin stitch while interior modeling is achieved by outline stitch and split stitch. This technique, which is here used with great artistry and painterly ability to create a variety of identifiable naturalistic flowers, is usually associated with Austrian embroidery, and, in particular, this set of vestments.[1] However, Lorenz Seelig has shown that the technique was also known in Munich and practiced in the court workshops there as evidenced by a chasuble with the coat-of-arms of Prince Maximilian III Joseph von Bayern, dated to 1745-1750.[2] This method of appliqué embroidery was also one favored by aristocratic Austrian ladies for their needlework.[3]

The intertwined 'ribbons' which border the vestments and outline areas on the dalmatics are embroidered with couched gold filé thread, purl, and paillettes. On the chalice veil, stole, and maniple the rayed crosses are worked with the same materials and embellished with applied metal discs. Each of the vestments is edged with a cord composed of silk and metal thread. All have been relined with a bright red silk satin, only the maniple retaining parts of the older lining. A small portion of the lining, c. ½ x 1⅞ inches or the size of a label or marking, has been cut from all but the cope.

The cope has a detachable shield which fastens by buttons covered with metallic thread. The area on the body of the cope beneath the shield has been left undecorated. The cope closes with a two-part morse of gilt metal with a rococo design of C scrolls and flowers of contemporary Austrian or German manufacture. The edge of the tabs which support the morse is covered with a woven galloon of silk and metal thread. The chalice veil is trimmed with a rich border of metallic lace. The neck border of the stole has been covered with white plain weave linen edged with bobbin lace. The condition of the vestments varies from excellent to good.

Slightly above the center on the shield of the cope and above the central bottom flowers on the back of both dalmatics appears a flower-like application of silver foil edged in silver purl and embroidered in gold purl and paillettes to read 17 MT 73. This inscription identifies the donor of the vestments as Maria Theresia (1717-1780, reigned 1740-1780), Archduchess of Austria and Queen of Hungary and Bohemia. She gave this extraordinary set of vestments to a convent for noble ladies which she founded in Prague and of which her eldest daughter, Maria Anna, was later abbess until 1791. Ten other vestments belonging to this set are now in the Schnütgen-Museum in Cologne. These are a cope, two dalmatics, two chasubles—all with the same monogram and date—and two stoles, two maniples, and a chalice veil.[4]

Maria Theresia was the benefactrice for other vestments, some of which were made from her ceremonial dresses. Examples include the cope, chasuble, and dalmatic now in the Zagreb Cathedral treasury. The dalmatic bears a similar metal application with the inscription 17 MT 75 and has the identical apparel shape as the Bass dalmatics.[5] Of all the royal gifts, however, none is as impressive as the Bass/Schnütgen set which has come to be known by the name of its donor as the *Maria Theresia Ornat.*

A.M.Z.

Dalmatic (63.59.3)   A: Front   B: Back

1. Moriz Dreger, "Die Maria Theresia-Paramenten-Ausstellung," *Kunst und Kunsthandwerk,* 7, 1904, p.331 (ill. another chasuble in this technique) and f.; and, by the same author, "Eine wiedergefundene Sticktechnik," *Zeitschrift für christliche Kunst,* 19, 1906, pp. 341-48.

2. Lorenz Seelig, *Kirchliche Schätze aus bayerischen Schlössern,* exh. cat., Residenzmuseum, Munich, Berlin 1984, p. 214.

3. Harriet Bridgeman and Elizabeth Drury, eds., *Needlework,* New York 1978, p. 224.

4. For descriptions, discussions, and illustrations of these vestments see Peter Bloch, "Ein Messornat der Kaiserin Maria Theresia," *Museen in Köln, Bulletin,* 1 [November 1962], p. 130 and cover illustration; Overstolzenhaus zu Köln, *Neuerweibungen der Kölner Museen 1962,* exh. cat., Overstolzenhaus, Cologne 1962, p. 34 and ill. p. 21; Christa C. Mayer Thurman, *Raiment for the Lord's Service,* exh. cat., Art Institute of Chicago, Chicago 1975, pp. 262-64, no. 132; Uwe Westfehling, *Schnütgen-Museum,* Cologne 1977, pp. 92-94, Sabine Czymmek, "Wiener Seidenkunst im Kölner Schnütgen Museum," *Alte und moderne Kunst,* 24, 1979, pp. 6-9.

5. Zdenka Munk, *Riznica zagrebacke katedrale,* exh. cat., Muzejski prostor, Zagreb 1983, pp. 92 and 135, 82 (ill.).

FLEMISH SCHOOL (probably Brussels)

First quarter of the sixteenth century

The city of Brussels has had a long and important history as a tapestry-weaving center; the oldest known document referring to tapestries produced there dates from 1379. During the fifteenth century, its manufacture of tapestries was overshadowed by the more prominent centers of Arras and Tournai, located near the present French-Belgian border. These other towns lost their dominant position when their primary patrons, the dukes of Burgundy, suffered military reversals that seriously weakened Burgundian power. Leadership in tapestry production at the end of the fifteenth century was then assumed by Brussels, the capital of the province of Brabant and the seat of Austro-Spanish power in the Low Countries. The city possessed all of the factors necessary to support a large-scale luxury industry: a flourishing economy, a stable government, wealthy patrons, gifted artists to create tapestry designs, and highly skilled weavers. These factors enabled Brussels to manufacture tapestries regarded as the finest in the world, which were in great demand by royalty, the nobility, princes of the church, and people of wealth. Early sixteenth-century Brussels tapestries were considered without peer for the excellence of their design and the perfection of their workmanship. It was inevitable that tapestry workshops in other cities would try to capitalize on the leading center's reputation by misrepresenting their products as being from Brussels. To protect both the buyer and the Brussels manufacturers, a law of 1528 decreed that all Brussels tapestries of a certain size and value be woven with the city mark of a red shield flanked by a pair of B's for Brussels-Brabant. Weavers were also required to weave into the tapestry either their own marks, which could be a cipher or initials, or the mark of the entrepreneur or merchant who had commissioned the piece. An enormous quantity of tapestries was produced in Brussels until the Netherlands' long and bloody struggle for independence from Spain (1568-1648) irreparably damaged the tapestry industry. The brutal measures employed by the Duke of Alva, Philip II's appointee to the governorship of the Low Countries, to repress the rebellion prompted many tapestry weavers to flee to other countries. There they established tapestry workshops which successfully competed with Brussels for clients. Although later rulers of the Spanish-controlled Netherlands tried to encourage and support the Brussels tapestry industry, it never regained its former glory.

The Tournament (79.129)

Woven in the first quarter of the sixteenth century.
Wool and silk, *438.6 x 701.7 (170 x 272).*
Warp: undyed wool, average of five warps per cm.
Weft: dyed wool and dyed silk.
The Bass *Tournament* tapestry is in fair condition, with broken warps throughout and numerous woven slits that need to be resewn, particularly between the border and the field. Fading is minimal, except in certain red areas, e.g., the pattern on the right knight's caparison, that have faded to beige. An examination of the tapestry from the front only indicates that the borders have been altered.

Provenance
Sackville-West family, Knole, Kent, England.
J. Pierpont Morgan, New York, 1911.
P. W. French and Company, New York, 1913.
Dr. and Mrs. Alexander Hamilton Rice, New York, 1919, loaned to the Metropolitan Museum of Art, New York (loan number 1820) from 1919-1923; displayed in the Armour Room.
Purchased from the estate sale of Mrs. Alexander Hamilton Rice, 1965 (Parke-Bernet Galleries, Inc., 22-23 October 1965, lot 346) by P. W. French and Company, New York, for John and Johanna Bass.

References
Catalogue of Twenty Renaissance Tapestries from the J. Pierpont Morgan Collection, compiled by Seymour de Ricci, Paris 1913, no. VI, p. 16, ill. opp.
Stella Rubenstein, "A Flemish Tapestry of the Early Sixteenth Century," *Art in America,* 8, 1920; pp. 47-51 (attributed to Jan van Roome; knights' identification; tournament tapestries).
D. T. Baird Wood, "The Hamilton Rice Tapestry Representing a Combat between Jacques de Lalaing and James, 9th and Last Earl of Douglas," *Art in America,* 8, 1920, pp. 302-7 (emblems; Lalaing-Douglas theory).
Phyllis Ackerman, *A Catalogue of Tapestries in the Collection of Frank Gair Macomber,* n.p., n.d.[c., 1928], pp. 29-32 (attributed to Jan van Roome; relationship to Bass tapestry).
American Art Association, Anderson Galleries, Inc., New York, 10-12 December 1936, lot 615 (Macomber tapestry; note on the *Tournament*).
Bass Catalogue 1973, No. 129.
Andrew Sinclair, *Corsair: The Life of J. Pierpont Morgan,* Boston and Toronto 1981, pp. 198-201.

Fig. 1: Detail, center. Knights on horseback.

Fig. 2: Detail, lower right. Figure of Turk, on right.

Hugh Sackville-West, Letter to Deborah Kraak, 30 July 1986 (knight's identification).

H. C. Marillier (with additions by later hands), Subject Catalogue of Tapestries, Victoria and Albert Museum London, ms., n.d., 50 vols., 'Court and Romance: Tournaments,' p. 129 (tentative attribution to Jan van Roome).

Exhibitions

Paris, Galerie J. Seligman, *Descriptions d'une Série de tapisséries gothiques appartenant a M. J. Pierpont Morgan,* (pref. Seymour de Ricci) October 1912, no. VI, pp. 29-30. New York, The Metropolitan Museum of Art, *Guide to the Loan Exhibition of the J. Pierpont Morgan Collection,* exh. cat., 1914, ill. opp. p. 27.

The subject of the *Tournament* is not the combat itself but the preceding moment when the two approaching knights rein in their beautifully caparisoned horses and exchange salutes before a king, his court, and a crowd of spectators. They will advance through the opening in the protective wooden chute onto the Tournament, or lists, and begin to fight. In this type of tournament, called a *Freiturnier,* the knights engaged in successive battles, beginning with lances, then continuing with swords, but in a single combat such as this the choice of weapons may have varied. The popularity of this sort of competition is documented in *The Fourth Tournament* woodcut of 1509 by Lucas Cranach the Elder (B. 127).

Special armor was required for a *Freiturnier*: a reinforcing buff, strapped to the helmet, protected the lower half of the face, and a large reinforce with an extended flange that also covered part of the face was worn on the left shoulder. The height of the reinforcing buff worn by the left knight has been inaccurately raised by the designer or weaver of this tapestry so that the knight's vision would have been completely obscured. Both helmets are decorated with an impractical but stylish cascade of plumes, known as a panache, ornamented with a wealth of pearl and lozenge pendants. The carefully detailed armor appears to be Flemish or South German, c. 1490-1510.[1]

The emblems of the knights appear on their banners and their horses' reins and chest straps (fig. 1). To the left, on a gold field, are crowned red hearts surrounded by pansies. At the base of the panache and on the banner, the heart is shown within a wooden press. The knight on the right bears the unusual emblems of a carafe-like watering can with holes in the bottom, called a *chantepleure,* named

after the supposed singing and weeping noises it made when shaken (see ref. Wood). His banner and sections of his sleeved tunic display a tear-drop motif, in a possible continuation of the mournful imagery of the *chantepleure.*

Various identities have been suggested for the two knights. A widely accepted theory proposed by D. T. Baird Wood (see ref.) is that the *Tournament* represents an historic combat between Jacques de Lalaing, a knight of Brabant, and James, ninth and last Earl of Douglas, held before the King of Scotland at Sterling on 25 February, 1449. Wood considered the key to this identification the rare imagery of the *chantepleure* in combination with the tear-drop emblems of the knight. Both may be indirectly associated with Jacques de Lalaing. They are not part of his family coat-of-arms (a shield gules, 10 lozenges argent cojoined 3,3,3,1), but rather are the melancholy emblems used by his childhood friend, Marie de Clèves, the wife of Charles d'Orléans. She and the chevalier were brought up together at the court of the Duke of Clèves. There is much speculation that she was the inspiration for the nameless lady of the *Pas de la Fontaine des Pleures* in whose honor Jacques de Lalaing often fought and whose emblems, Wood asserted, identify that knight in the Bass *Tournament.*

The exploits of this renowned member of the Order of the Golden Fleece are chronicled in *Le livre des faits de Jacques de Lalain,* by Lefèbvre de Saint-Rémis, herald of the Golden Fleece, (once attributed to Georges Chastellain).[2] One chapter recounts in stirring detail the Scottish tournament. Wood concluded that it is the crowned heart of the Douglas coat-of-arms that appears as the emblem of the other knight in the *Tournament.*

Emblems, however, are not a totally reliable means of identification. In documented examples, knights do not consistently use the same emblem in every tournament. Wood's association of the *chantepleure* and tears with Jacques de Lalaing does not explain why another emblem of Marie de Clèves, the pansy, decorates the banner and horse caparison of his opponent. Another reason to urge caution in accepting Wood's hypothesis is the fact that the crowned heart was a popular emblem, and was not unique to the Douglas clan. For example, it is used for the Garis de Troguern family of Brittany and the Henskens family of Brabant (see ref. Rubenstein). The archives of the Sackville-West family (the first documented owners of the Bass *Tournament*) identify one knight as the Earl of Douglas, adding in parentheses "Duke of Tourraine," but label his opponent a "Burgundian Duke de Rethel" (see ref. Sackville-West). In lieu of documentary evidence for the tapestry's commission and a more thorough study of fifteenth- and sixteenth-century heraldry and emblems, Wood's identification of the two knights in the tapestry as Jacques de Lalaing and James, Earl of Douglas, will remain an intriguing hypothesis.

The designer of the splendid *Tournament* tapestry is likewise unknown. A clue to his identity was once thought to be found on the garments of the exotic figure standing in the lower right corner, identified as a Turk by his turban, beard, and scimitar (fig. 2). The inscriptions on the decorative bands of his robes attracted the attention of early twentieth-century tapestry historians who believed the signature of artist Jan van Roome was discernible in the mixture of Roman letters with those suggestive of Kufic, Greek, or Hebrew (see refs. Rubenstein, Ackerman, and Marillier). Within the uppermost lettered band, Stella Rubenstein, in her 1920 article, isolated the letters "IAN ROI." She asserted that this was a variation on Jan van Roome's signature, citing the putative woven signatures of the artist compiled by A. Thiéry.[3] Her attribution lost credibility with the 1927 publication of Marthe Crick-Kuntziger's well-documented refutation of Thiéry's claim.[4] Current tapestry scholarship still exercises extreme caution in assigning authorship of tapestry designs when inscriptions, such as that in the *Tournament,* are incomplete, illegible, or deformed. Of the many tapestries formerly attributed to Jan van Roome, only the famous *Herkinbald* in the Musées Royaux d'Art et d'Histoire, Brussels, can be definitely attributed to his oeuvre.

Fanciful inscriptions were common decorative motifs on hems, sleeves, and coifs in the Franco-Flemish territories at the end of the fifteenth and the beginning of the sixteenth century. Inspired by Islamic calligraphy on imported textiles or ceramics, bands of lettering on Western costumes and textiles created an aura of exoticism. On actors' costumes, inscriptions could often identify a character by name, or evoke an Eastern atmosphere simply by their alien quality.[5] As for the Turk in the *Tournament,* the conspicuous and singular use of inscription bands with virtually indecipherable lettering heightens the air of Oriental mystery created by his vesture. His role in this chivalric spectacle remains a mystery.

Tournaments have been the subject of many fifteenth and sixteenth-century tapestries (see ref. Rubenstein).

Perhaps the most famous sixteenth-century *Freiturnier* tapestry is located in the Musée des Beaux-Arts, Valenciennes. Unlike the single combat depicted in the Bass tapestry, a group of knights compete in a crowded tournament field littered with discarded reinforcing buffs, and broken lances. Its more Renaissance-inspired treatment of form and space also distinguishes it from the *Tournament.* More closely related to the Bass tapestry in both style and composition is an early sixteenth-century tapestry fragment sold by P. W. French and Co., New York, to William B. Sloane in 1920.[6] Similarities include the general format of a joust between two plume-crowned knights staged before a king and his court, as well as the shared detail of tear-shaped emblems worn by a knight in each tapestry. Another tapestry from the same period, formerly in the collection of Frank Gair Macomber, was erroneously identified as *The Duke of Burgundy Greets Jacques de Lalaing,* solely because of the tear-drop pendants in the knight's panache (see refs. Ackerman and American Art Association). This ornamentation, however, was not an emblem of Jacques de Lalaing but rather a popular decoration for the plumed headgear of knights and gentlemen alike.

D.E.K.

1. I am grateful to Donald J. LaRocca, assistant curator, Department of Arms and Armor, Metropolitan Museum of Art, for his generous assistance with information on the *Freiturnier* arms and armor.
2. H.M.B.J.L. Kervyn de Lettenhove, ed., *Oeuvres de Georges Chastellain,* vol. 8, Brussels 1866, pp. 164-79.
3. A. Thiéry, *Les inscriptions et signatures des tapisséries du peintre bruxellois Jean de Bruxelles appelé aussi Jean de Rome,* Louvain 1907.
4. Marthe Crick-Kuntziger, *Maître Knoest et les tapisséries 'signées' des Musées Royaux de Cinquantenaire,* Liège 1927.
5. Jan-Karel Steppe, "Inscriptions decoratives contenant des signatures et des mentions du lieu d'origine sur des tapisséries bruxelloises de la fin du XVe et du début du XVIe siècle," Musées Royaux d'Art et d'Histoire. *Tapisséries bruxelloises de la pré-Renaissance,* exh. cat., 1976, pp. 193-230.
6. Information obtained from the J. Paul Getty Center for the History of Art and the Humanities, Photo Archives, Decorative Arts Section, Santa Monica, California.

LOUIS-MARIE BAADER, Designer

French, 1828–c. 1919

BRAQUENIÉ ET CIE, Manufactory

Malines, Belgium

Two tapestries:
The Start for the Hunt (64.95)
The Return from the Hunt (64.96)
Woven in the last quarter of the 19th century.

Both signed, lower right: *L. BAADER.*
                    lower left: *BRAQUENIÉ et CIE*
Cotton (?) warp, wool and silk weft; 7-8 warps per cm.,
19 warps per inch; *450 x 1437.5 (184 x 575).*
The tapestries are finely woven, with highly individualized
figures in bright colors against a muted background. They
are in excellent condition.

Provenance
Purchased for The Bass Collection from French & Co., Inc.,
New York, 1963.

References
Bass Catalogue 1973, nos. 95 and 96.

Exhibitions
Antwerp, Exposition Universelle, 1885.

In *The Start for the Hunt,* lords and ladies in medieval dress
set out from a turreted castle on fine steeds with decorative
trappings. Although one of the gentlemen carries a lance
and another lifts his falcon on high, it is the attendants on
foot who shoulder the cross-bow and manage the hunting
animals: trim and quick dogs to chase the stag; strong and
powerful ones with spiked collars for attacking the boar;
and hooded falcons, which sit on two wheels, to hunt birds.

In *The Return from the Hunt,* the party travels through
an autumnal landscape toward the distant castle. At right
the man on horseback sounds a horn to announce their
return. The success of the hunt is evident from the stag
and birds at left, and the boar trussed on poles. The court
jester, with game over his shoulder and a dog on a leash,
accompanies the party. The larger dogs bark at a trio of
peasants, two children and their father, who watch the
entourage.

The tapestries were designed by Louis-Marie Baader,
a French artist with a variety of styles. Born in Lannion, he
was a student of Yvon and specialized in mythological and
historical scenes as well as genre painting. He exhibited at
the Paris Salon from 1857 until 1914, taking a third class
medal in 1874. His style as represented in these tapestries
is similar to that of his better-known contemporary, Willem
Geets (1838-1919), who specialized in historical subjects
and whose work was particularly well-suited for adaptation
into tapestry. From Malines, Geets was also associated with
the Braquenié manufactory in that city.

The brothers H. and A. Braquenié, originally from
Tournai, first established themselves in Paris. In 1856
they became associated with the low-warp tapestry atelier
founded by the Comte des Cantons de Montblanc in
Inglemuster, and, following his death in 1861, they
continued the association with his widow and son. In 1879
the brothers left to establish in Malines a manufactory
which was sustained primarily by orders from the Belgian
government and regional administrators. Most of the
subjects of these tapestries are drawn from national or
local history. This prefigures a similar trend in patriotic
themes which would flourish in the late nineteenth and
twentieth centuries and be evident in tapestries made in
most European countries and in America. The
manufactory exhibited numerous pieces to high acclaim at
the Exposition Universelle of 1878.[1] These two tapestries
were awarded first prize in Antwerp in 1885.

The Braquenié atelier was only one of a number of
tapestry workshops in Belgium in the late nineteenth
century. An in-depth study of the industry needs to
be written for the role of the Braquenié manufactory to
be better evaluated and understood.

A.M.Z.

1. Jules Guiffrey, *Histoire de la tapisserie,* Tours 1886, pp. 480-81, and
   G. van Doorslaer, "La fabrication de tapisséries artistiques à
   Malines," *Académie royale d'archéologie de Belgique, Annales,* ser. 7
   (3-4), 1925, pp. 42-3, discuss the Braquenié manufactory and other
   Belgian ateliers.

Numerical Index of Paintings

NUMERICAL INDEX TO TEXTILES

CHANGES OF ATTRIBUTION

Current Attributions 1990		Former Attributions 1973
Paintings		
Antwerp School, 16th century, attributed to	63.18	Heinrich Aldegrever, attributed to
Austrian/German School (Salzburg or Passau), 15th century attributed to	79.133	Gabriel Maleskircher
Giovanni Barbagelata	63.17	Giovanni Massoni
Thomas Barker	64.112	George Morland, attributed to
Carlo Dolci, Manner of	79.218	Unknown 18th century Master
Anthony van Dyck, after	63.38	William Dobson
Anthony van Dyck, Follower of	63.36	Anthony van Dyck, attributed to
Anthony van Dyck, Style of	67.97	Anthony van Dyck, attributed to
French/Spanish School 15th century, attributed to	63.28	Aragonese School
German School, c. 1600	63.30	Master of Messkirch, attributed to
German School, last quarter of 16th century	79.185	Christoph Amberger
Domenico Ghirlandaio, Workshop	63.25	Sebastiano Mainardi, attributed to
El Greco, Studio of	63.5	El Greco, attributed to
Italian School (Lombard), 17th century, attributed to	79.236	Unknown 17th century Master
Jacob Jordaens	79.275	Peter Paul Rubens
Jean-Baptiste van Loo, attributed to	79.132	Jean-Marc Nattier
Michiel van Musscher	63.2	Johannes Vermeer, attributed to
Johann Baptist Reiter	79.187	Viennese Master, c. 1820
Peter Paul Rubens and Studio	63.9	Peter Paul Rubens
Peter Paul Rubens, Studio	63.8	Peter Paul Rubens
Sebastiano del Piombo, after	63.23	Sebastiano del Piombo
Bernhard Strigel, Workshop or Circle of	63.21/22	Swabian Master, Collaborator of Hans Multscher, c. 1470
Titian, after	63.27	Polidoro Lanzano (Lanciano)
Titian, after	63.13	Anthony van Dyck
Textiles		
Spain (probably Toledo) second quarter 16th century	79.426	Italian, c. 1600
Italy, 17th century	79.140	Italian, 15th century

List of Artists

Works Executed Before 1840

Antwerp School, attributed to
Austrian or South German School (Salzburg or Passau),
    attributed to
Giovanni Barbagelata
Thomas Barker
Ferdinand Bol
Sandro Botticelli and Domenico Ghirlandaio
Sandro Botticelli, Workshop
Cornelis Cornelisz van Haarlem
Carlo Dolci, Manner of
Anthony van Dyck, after
Anthony van Dyck, Follower of
Anthony van Dyck, Style of
Flemish School, sixteenth century
Govert Flinck
French/Spanish School, fifteenth century, attributed to
German School, c. 1600
German School, last quarter of the sixteenth century
Domenico Ghirlandaio, Workshop
El Greco (Dominikos Theotokopulos), Studio of
John Hoppner, R.A.
Italian School (Lombard), attributed to
Jacob Jordaens
Marcellus Koffermans
Sir Thomas Lawrence, P.R.A.
Jean-Baptiste van Loo, attributed to
Master of the Revaler St. Elizabeth Legend
Michiel van Musscher
William Owen, A.R.A.
Hyacinthe Rigaud
George Romney
Peter Paul Rubens and Studio
Peter Paul Rubens, Studio
Peter Paul Rubens, after
Sebastiano del Piombo, after
Gerard Seghers
Spanish School (Aragonese), attributed to
Bernhard Strigel, Workshop or Circle of

Titian, after
Jan Weenix
Benjamin West, P.R.A.
Henry Wyatt

Works Executed After 1840

Otto Barth
Gyulia Benczur
Arnold Clementschitsch
Eugène Delacroix, attributed to
Leo Delitz
Jules Dupré
Jehudo Epstein
Jean-Baptiste Armand Guillaumin
Eugen (Eugène) Jettel
Maximilian Kurzweil
Hans Makart
Emanuel Notterman, manner of
Adolf Pichler
Edmund Pick-Morino (alias for Oedon Pick)
Emil Rau
Johann Baptist Reiter
Franz Schrotzberg
Ferdinand Stransky
Heinrich Tomec
Eduard Veith

Ecclesiastical Needlework

Spain, Altar Frontal
Italy, Chasuble
Austria (Vienna), Bishop's Mitre
Austria (Vienna), Rosenornat
Austria (Vienna), Maria Theresia Ornat

Tapestries

Flemish School
Louis-Marie Baader, Designer; Braquenié et Cie,
    Manufactory